Flights Near and Far

Language Patterns

Tracing Our Letters
Listening Letters
Laughing Letters
Magic Letters
Adventures with Mac

Working with Letters
Book 1 Book 2

Creative Pictures

Silver Steps
Golden Trails

Wings of Wonder
Flights Near and Far

Illustrations by:
Hedy Campbell
Ralph Campbell
Ann Chestnut
Heather Cooper
Alan Daniel
Brian Ewing
Doreen Foster
Bob Frank
John Luckhurst
Patrice Parkinson
Aileen Richardson
Barry Rubin
Louise Sheppard
Stewart Sherwood
Merle Smith
Mike Yazzolino

Cover Design by:
Bob Frank

Photographs by:
Arabian American Oil Company, *p. 82*
The Bettmann Archive, *pp. 97, 268, 272, 273, 274, 276, 277*
Ralph Campbell
Carolina Biological Supply Company, *p. 81*
Gail Johnstone
Mercury Illustration Research, *pp. 94, 96, 98*
Miller Services, *pp. 74, 75, 83, 267*
National Aeronautics and Space Administration, *pp. viii, 1*

ISBN 0-03-923890-3
Printed in Canada 1 2 3 4 5 74 73 72 71 70

Dr. John R. Linn
Dorothy Donaldson
Anne Saunders

Mabel Bruce
Jean Ellis
Janet Trischuk

FLIGHTS NEAR AND FAR

Holt, Rinehart and Winston of Canada, Limited
Toronto   Montreal

Acknowledgements

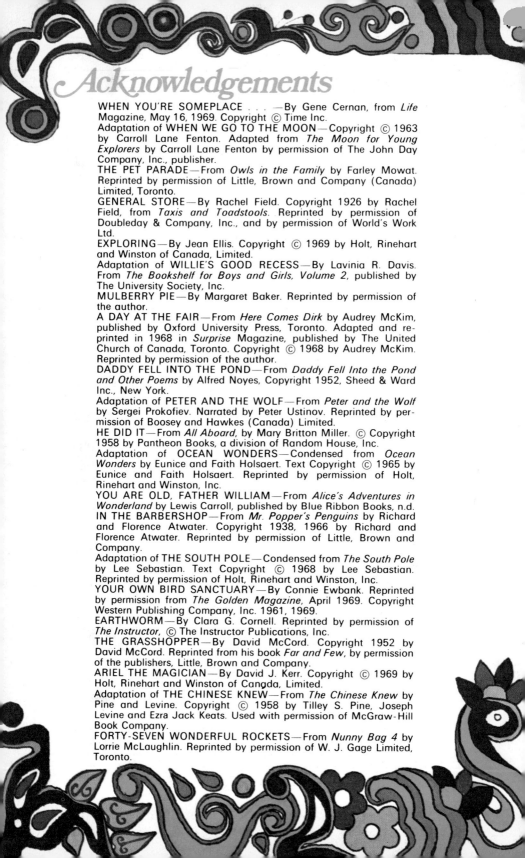

WHEN YOU'RE SOMEPLACE . . . —By Gene Cernan, from *Life* Magazine, May 16, 1969. Copyright © Time Inc.

Adaptation of WHEN WE GO TO THE MOON—Copyright © 1963 by Carroll Lane Fenton. Adapted from *The Moon for Young Explorers* by Carroll Lane Fenton by permission of The John Day Company, Inc., publisher.

THE PET PARADE—From *Owls in the Family* by Farley Mowat. Reprinted by permission of Little, Brown and Company (Canada) Limited, Toronto.

GENERAL STORE—By Rachel Field. Copyright 1926 by Rachel Field, from *Taxis and Toadstools*. Reprinted by permission of Doubleday & Company, Inc., and by permission of World's Work Ltd.

EXPLORING—By Jean Ellis. Copyright © 1969 by Holt, Rinehart and Winston of Canada, Limited.

Adaptation of WILLIE'S GOOD RECESS—By Lavinia R. Davis. From *The Bookshelf for Boys and Girls, Volume 2*, published by The University Society, Inc.

MULBERRY PIE—By Margaret Baker. Reprinted by permission of the author.

A DAY AT THE FAIR—From *Here Comes Dirk* by Audrey McKim, published by Oxford University Press, Toronto. Adapted and reprinted in 1968 in *Surprise* Magazine, published by The United Church of Canada, Toronto. Copyright © 1968 by Audrey McKim. Reprinted by permission of the author.

DADDY FELL INTO THE POND—From *Daddy Fell Into the Pond and Other Poems* by Alfred Noyes, Copyright 1952, Sheed & Ward Inc., New York.

Adaptation of PETER AND THE WOLF—From *Peter and the Wolf* by Sergei Prokofiev. Narrated by Peter Ustinov. Reprinted by permission of Boosey and Hawkes (Canada) Limited.

HE DID IT—From *All Aboard*, by Mary Britton Miller. © Copyright 1958 by Pantheon Books, a division of Random House, Inc.

Adaptation of OCEAN WONDERS—Condensed from *Ocean Wonders* by Eunice and Faith Holsaert. Text Copyright © 1965 by Eunice and Faith Holsaert. Reprinted by permission of Holt, Rinehart and Winston, Inc.

YOU ARE OLD, FATHER WILLIAM—From *Alice's Adventures in Wonderland* by Lewis Carroll, published by Blue Ribbon Books, n.d.

IN THE BARBERSHOP—From *Mr. Popper's Penguins* by Richard and Florence Atwater. Copyright 1938, 1966 by Richard and Florence Atwater. Reprinted by permission of Little, Brown and Company.

Adaptation of THE SOUTH POLE—Condensed from *The South Pole* by Lee Sebastian. Text Copyright © 1968 by Lee Sebastian. Reprinted by permission of Holt, Rinehart and Winston, Inc.

YOUR OWN BIRD SANCTUARY—By Connie Ewbank. Reprinted by permission from *The Golden Magazine*, April 1969. Copyright Western Publishing Company, Inc. 1961, 1969.

EARTHWORM—By Clara G. Cornell. Reprinted by permission of *The Instructor*, © The Instructor Publications, Inc.

THE GRASSHOPPER—By David McCord. Copyright 1952 by David McCord. Reprinted from his book *Far and Few*, by permission of the publishers, Little, Brown and Company.

ARIEL THE MAGICIAN—By David J. Kerr. Copyright © 1969 by Holt, Rinehart and Winston of Cangda, Limited.

Adaptation of THE CHINESE KNEW—From *The Chinese Knew* by Pine and Levine. Copyright © 1958 by Tilley S. Pine, Joseph Levine and Ezra Jack Keats. Used with permission of McGraw-Hill Book Company.

FORTY-SEVEN WONDERFUL ROCKETS—From *Nunny Bag 4* by Lorrie McLaughlin. Reprinted by permission of W. J. Gage Limited, Toronto.

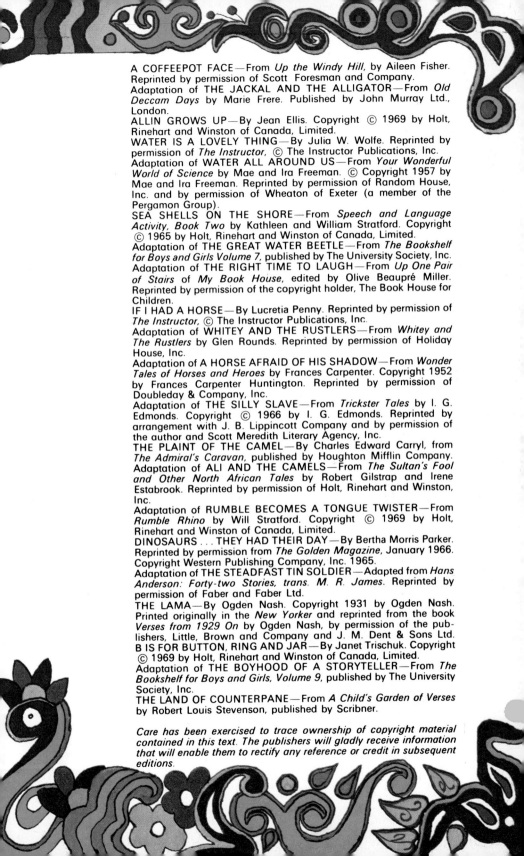

A COFFEEPOT FACE—From *Up the Windy Hill*, by Aileen Fisher. Reprinted by permission of Scott Foresman and Company.

Adaptation of THE JACKAL AND THE ALLIGATOR—From *Old Deccam Days* by Marie Frere. Published by John Murray Ltd., London.

ALLIN GROWS UP—By Jean Ellis. Copyright © 1969 by Holt, Rinehart and Winston of Canada, Limited.

WATER IS A LOVELY THING—By Julia W. Wolfe. Reprinted by permission of *The Instructor*, © The Instructor Publications, Inc.

Adaptation of WATER ALL AROUND US—From *Your Wonderful World of Science* by Mae and Ira Freeman. © Copyright 1957 by Mae and Ira Freeman. Reprinted by permission of Random House, Inc. and by permission of Wheaton of Exeter (a member of the Pergamon Group).

SEA SHELLS ON THE SHORE—From *Speech and Language Activity, Book Two* by Kathleen and William Stratford. Copyright © 1965 by Holt, Rinehart and Winston of Canada, Limited.

Adaptation of THE GREAT WATER BEETLE—From *The Bookshelf for Boys and Girls Volume 7*, published by The University Society, Inc.

Adaptation of THE RIGHT TIME TO LAUGH—From *Up One Pair of Stairs* of *My Book House*, edited by Olive Beaupré Miller. Reprinted by permission of the copyright holder, The Book House for Children.

IF I HAD A HORSE—By Lucretia Penny. Reprinted by permission of *The Instructor*, © The Instructor Publications, Inc.

Adaptation of WHITEY AND THE RUSTLERS—From *Whitey and The Rustlers* by Glen Rounds. Reprinted by permission of Holiday House, Inc.

Adaptation of A HORSE AFRAID OF HIS SHADOW—From *Wonder Tales of Horses and Heroes* by Frances Carpenter. Copyright 1952 by Frances Carpenter Huntington. Reprinted by permission of Doubleday & Company, Inc.

Adaptation of THE SILLY SLAVE—From *Trickster Tales* by I. G. Edmonds. Copyright © 1966 by I. G. Edmonds. Reprinted by arrangement with J. B. Lippincott Company and by permission of the author and Scott Meredith Literary Agency, Inc.

THE PLAINT OF THE CAMEL—By Charles Edward Carryl, from *The Admiral's Caravan*, published by Houghton Mifflin Company.

Adaptation of ALI AND THE CAMELS—From *The Sultan's Fool and Other North African Tales* by Robert Gilstrap and Irene Estabrook. Reprinted by permission of Holt, Rinehart and Winston, Inc.

Adaptation of RUMBLE BECOMES A TONGUE TWISTER—From *Rumble Rhino* by Will Stratford. Copyright © 1969 by Holt, Rinehart and Winston of Canada, Limited.

DINOSAURS . . . THEY HAD THEIR DAY—By Bertha Morris Parker. Reprinted by permission from *The Golden Magazine*, January 1966. Copyright Western Publishing Company, Inc. 1965.

Adaptation of THE STEADFAST TIN SOLDIER—Adapted from *Hans Anderson: Forty-two Stories*, trans. M. R. James. Reprinted by permission of Faber and Faber Ltd.

THE LAMA—By Ogden Nash. Copyright 1931 by Ogden Nash. Printed originally in the *New Yorker* and reprinted from the book *Verses from 1929 On* by Ogden Nash, by permission of the publishers, Little, Brown and Company and J. M. Dent & Sons Ltd.

B IS FOR BUTTON, RING AND JAR—By Janet Trischuk. Copyright © 1969 by Holt, Rinehart and Winston of Canada, Limited.

Adaptation of THE BOYHOOD OF A STORYTELLER—From *The Bookshelf for Boys and Girls, Volume 9*, published by The University Society, Inc.

THE LAND OF COUNTERPANE—From *A Child's Garden of Verses* by Robert Louis Stevenson, published by Scribner.

Care has been exercised to trace ownership of copyright material contained in this text. The publishers will gladly receive information that will enable them to rectify any reference or credit in subsequent editions.

Contents

"When you're someplace that is new and exciting,

someplace you maybe never expected to be,

someplace you're not sure is real,

you almost pinch yourself and tell yourself,

"This is happening right now."

Gene Cernan

When We Go to the Moon

Where and How Far

When we take a trip in a car
a road map shows where we are going
and how far we must drive to get there.
Road maps do not go as far as the moon,
but we know where to find it.
The moon is a satellite (SAT eh lite).
It goes round the earth in an oval path
which we call its orbit (OR bit).
We can always find the moon
in the proper part of its orbit
at any special time on any special day.
Though we know just where to find the moon,
its orbit is very, very large.
In fact, it is so big that the moon
never comes closer to the earth
than 221,000 miles.
In the opposite part of its orbit
the moon is 252,000 miles away.
It is much farther than any distance
we can travel on the earth.

How Big Is the Moon?
When the moon comes up in the east
it looks bigger than trees or houses.
Then, as the moon goes high in the sky,
it seems to become so small
that we can cover it with a dime.
This does not really happen, of course,
for we know that the moon is solid
and cannot change its shape or size
The moon also is many times larger
than a dime, a building, or a tree.
Scientists who have studied the moon
say it is a ball-shaped world
more than 2,100 miles in thickness.
This tells us that the moon is more
than one fourth as large as the earth.
The biggest building in the world
is much smaller than the moon.

Our Pointed Spaceship
When we take trips on the earth
we ride in cars, trains, or airplanes.
Since these things cannot go to the moon
we shall travel in a spaceship
that will look like one of these.

Each spaceship is short and pointed.
It sits on top of a module (MOD yool)
that is longer and contains engines
as well as the fuel they will use.
The ship is insulated (IN su LAY ted)
to protect us from heat and cold.
Insulation also keeps out dangerous rays
that come from the sun.
If these rays could get into the spaceship
they would make us very ill.

The Moon Rocket

There are engines in the module
below our spaceship,
but they do not have enough power
to take us to the moon.
This power will come from a huge rocket
that is taller than a building
with thirty stories, or "floors".
Men fasten our spaceship and its module
to the tip of this big rocket.
Then, when we are ready to go,
an elevator that runs in a tower
takes us up to the door of the ship.
When we look out of the elevator
we see that the rocket is made
of sections, which are called stages.
Each stage contains engines that work
until they use all their fuel.
When the fuel in a stage has been used
that part of the rocket drops off.
Then the engines in the next stage
begin to fire and use their fuel.
They drive the ship, with its module,
and all that is left of the rocket,
onward toward the moon.

Our Trip Begins

We fasten ourselves into our seats
and tell the captain we are ready.
Boo-oom! go the engines of Stage One
as they "blast off" from the earth.
Up goes the rocket with our spaceship.
Stage One uses its fuel and falls off,
and Stage Two follows a few minutes later.
Stage Three engines then start
but the captain soon stops them,
and we "coast" partway round the earth.
Coasting lets the crew make sure
that everything in our spaceship
is working as it should work.
If something is wrong, the ship can turn
and go back to the ground.

The Speed of Escape

Soon a crewman calls "Okay sir!"
and our captain starts the engines.
They make the ship go still faster
until it reaches the speed of escape.
This means that we are travelling
almost 25,000 miles per hour.
At this speed our spaceship can turn away,
or "escape", from the earth
and can travel to the moon
or go still farther away into space.
But if we could not reach this speed
the earth would not let us escape.
Instead, it would pull and pull
until our spaceship would turn
and come back toward the earth.

Aiming for the Moon

We have "escaped" from the earth,
but we notice that our spaceship
is not going toward the moon.
When we ask, the captain tells us why.
"You know," he explains, "that the moon
travels round and round the earth.
The moon takes almost a month
to make one complete trip
at a speed of 2,000 miles per hour.
We are moving much faster than that,
but our ship will slow down as it goes
farther and farther away from the earth.
We also have a long way to travel—
at least 220,000 miles
before we come to the moon's orbit.
We'll take about thirty-four hours
to travel this distance—
and during all that time the moon
will be whirling around the earth
at its speed of 2,000 miles per hour.
If we aim our ship toward the place
where the moon is right now
we'll have to turn and follow the moon
or it will leave us far, far behind.
To prevent this, we aim at the place
where the moon will be
about thirty-four hours from now.
In this way we will meet the moon.
We'll not let it leave us behind
while we are travelling toward it."

The Sky Darkens

It was daytime when we left the earth
but the sky has turned dark as night.

Daytime skies are bright on the earth
because it is covered with air.
The air sometimes seems to be nothing,
but it really is made up
of tiny bits, or particles of gas
that are called molecules (MOL eh kyoolz).
They catch sunlight and reflect it
into every part of the sky
and into shady places on the ground.

But there is no air out here in space,
and sunlight is not reflected.
This leaves the sky as dark as night
except where light comes to us
from the stars, the moon, and the sun.
Since the air does not catch their light
they shine much more brightly
than they ever shine on earth.
This explains why the moon
now shows so plainly, and why we see
a bright "crown", or corona (ko RO nah)
that spreads out around the sun.

The Face of the Moon

As the moon travels along its orbit,
it keeps one half toward the earth.
We call this half the face of the moon.
We have looked at it through telescopes
but we see it more and more plainly
as we whiz through space.
First we look at the big dark places
which form the eyes, nose, and ears
of the make-believe Man in the Moon.
People once supposed
that these places were water
and gave them a name that means "seas".
Scientists still use this name
though they know that the "seas" are land
and are covered with dark-coloured rock.
The first moon landing was made
in one of these seas
known as the Sea of Tranquility.
Both the "seas" and the "lands"
are dotted with craters (KRAY terz),
which look like cups, bowls, or saucers
surrounded by rings of hills or mountains.
We also see long ridges and mountains
that are not arranged in rings.
Low places between these mountains
are valleys that usually wind to and fro.
Dark lines, however, are cracks
but bright spots are covered with fine dust.

Daytime and Night

We know that the earth turns round
once in every twenty-four hours,
causing daytime and night.
The moon turns round and round, too,

but it does not go as fast as the earth.
The moon takes almost a month
to make one complete turn.
That is as long a time as the moon
takes to travel around its orbit.
This means that daytime on the moon
lasts about two of our weeks,
and night lasts about two weeks more.
Do you think you would like to live
on a slowly turning world
where daytime and night last so long?

Carroll Lane Fenton

THE PET PARADE

On the day school closed for the summer, the T. Eaton Department Store announced it was going to sponsor a pet parade two weeks later, and there were going to be prizes for the most interesting pets, and the best displays. Bruce was the first of our gang to hear about it, and he came right over to my house to tell Murray and me.

"Hey!" said Bruce, after he had told us all he knew. "With the animals we got, we could win a dozen prizes. What about it?"

Murray and I didn't need much convincing. We spent the next couple of days planning what we'd do.

First we decided to hitch Mutt and Rex to my old express wagon. We would fix it up with coloured cardboard and stuff, so it looked like a circus wagon. We planned to put an old fur muff of my mother's around Mutt's neck to make him look like a lion, and we were going to paint black stripes on Rex so he would look like a zebra. Then we decided to build a circus cage on the wagon, and fill it with different kinds of gophers. Finally, we decided to have the owls riding on top of the cage, all dressed up in dolls' clothes.

We had two weeks to get things ready, and we really worked.

First we built the circus cage, and when we were finished it looked just like the real ones that used to come to Saskatoon with the Bailey Brothers Circus every summer. Ours wasn't as strong, though, because the sides were only cardboard, painted red and blue and yellow. And instead of iron bars, we used chicken wire to keep the gophers from getting out.

When it was finished we made a hike out to the bluffs near the exhibition grounds, because that was a good place to find wood gophers. We caught six of them, and on the way home we snared about a dozen striped gophers that were living in a cutbank by the roadside. Together with the thirty ordinary gophers we already had, this added up to an awful lot of gophers, and there wasn't going to be room for all of them in one circus cage.

Murray fixed that.

"Why don't we make another cage out of my wagon?" he suggested. "Then we'd have twice as much chance to win first prize."

It was a dandy idea. so we went ahead and built the second cage. Then we decided to put some of our white rats with the extra gophers in the second one, to make it different.

The day before the parade—which was a Saturday—we had everything ready. I had borrowed some dolls' clothes from Faith Honigan, who lived on the next block. Murray had got some washable sign paint from his Dad, so he could paint the black stripes on Rex. We had found a set of real dog harness for Mutt, and we had made a second set for Rex, out of twine. The cage wagons were all finished and stored away in our garage so they wouldn't get wet if it rained.

On Sunday morning, I didn't even wait to eat my breakfast before I rushed out to the garage. Murray was already there, but Bruce didn't come along for about an hour, and we were getting worried he might not make it at all. By the time he showed up we had the gophers and the white rats all loaded and I was trying to get the dolls' clothes on the owls. Bruce came into the yard with a shoebox under his arm, and a big grin on his face.

"Hi-eee!" he shouted. "I guess we'll win the first prize sure. Bet you can't guess what I have in this box?"

Murray and I couldn't guess. I shook the box a couple of times, and whatever was inside was pretty heavy. I was just going to untie the string and open it when Bruce grabbed it away from me.

"No, sir," he said. "Don't you do that! We might never catch this critter again!"

"Aw, come on!" I begged him. "What you got in there, anyway? Come on, Brucie. You have to tell us."

"Don't have to—don't aim to!" Bruce said. "Just you wait and see."

Murray and I pretended we didn't care what he had in his shoebox anyway. I went back to putting the dolls' clothes on the owls, and it wasn't easy. Weeps just stood there and whimpered while I pulled a pink dress over his head and pinned a floppy hat on him. But Wol took one look at the sailor suit I had for him. Then he rumpled himself up into a ball and began to clack his beak and hiss. It took two of us to hold him down while we got him dressed, and by the time we were finished he was in a terrible temper.

We couldn't trust him to stay quietly on the wagon-top after all that fuss, so we decided to tie him to it with some twine around his legs. That made him madder still.

While Bruce and I were working on the owls, Murray was trying to paint the stripes on Rex. Rex didn't like it, and there was about as much black paint on Murray as on the dog. Then Murray said he might as well finish what Rex had started, so he smeared black paint all over his own face and said he would go in the parade as a Zulu warrior.

Just before we were ready to start for downtown, Bruce took the paintbrush and printed some words on the shoebox; then he tied the box to the top of the second wagon. What he printed was:

SUrpriIS PET Do NOt FeEED

We harnessed up the dogs, with Mutt leading because he knew how to pull in harness and Rex didn't. Rex didn't seem to want to learn, either. He kept pulling off to one side, and every time he did it he almost upset the wagons. We had an awful time getting our outfit all the way downtown and we were nearly late for the parade,

which started at ten o'clock. One thing, though: by the time we did get there, old Rex was just about worn out and he stopped acting like a bucking bronco.

The parade formed in front of the Carnegie Public Library and then it was supposed to go about six blocks to the T. Eaton Store, where the judges' stand was.

It seemed like a million kids were there with every kind of pet you ever saw. One little boy, about five years old, was leading a Clydesdale horse as big as an elephant, and the horse had "BABY" on the blanket it was wearing. If that thing was a baby, I hope to eat it!

There were a lot of goats, and it was a hot day, and you could smell goats all over Saskatoon. Some of the girls were wheeling cats along in baby carriages, and the cats were wearing silly hats and were pinned down under lacy covers. Some of them were yowling fit to scare the dead. There were more dogs than you could shake a stick at—every kind of dog you ever heard about, and a lot of kinds that nobody ever heard about.

Right in the middle of the parade was a boy leading a pet skunk on a string. He had the middle of the parade all to himself, too. Nobody was crowding him!

There were pet rabbits, ducks, chickens, geese, a couple of pigs, and a bunch of pedigree calves. There was even one little boy carrying a quart jar full of water, with a bunch of tadpoles swimming around in it.

You'd expect lots of trouble, what with all the animals and the fact that it was a hot day and everybody was excited and there was so much noise. But there really wasn't much trouble. There were dogfights, of course; and one dog, who wasn't even in the parade at all, made a go for a cat in a baby carriage and that stampeded one of the goats. But some salesmen from the store were in the parade too, and they got things quieted down, though one of them got bitten on the leg a little bit.

It took about an hour for our outfit to get opposite the judges' stand. There were five judges; some were women and some, men. The Mayor of Saskatoon was one of them. There were two Mounties beside the stand, dressed in their red coats. A lot of parents were jammed up against the stand too, so they could cheer if their kids won a prize.

I'd had a good look at the parade by then, and there wasn't an outfit that had a patch on ours. We were sure to win a good prize, and I figured it would be first prize. We had a little trouble when we got to the stand, though, because Rex was so tired he just lay down and wouldn't get up again. But that only made the judges laugh, and they came down from the stand to take a good look at our entry.

I overheard one of the woman judges tell another woman that ours was the best rig she had seen, and, "Isn't it cute the way it's decked out just like a real circus?" The first prize seemed to be right in our pockets, when the president of the T. Eaton Store, who was also one of the judges, saw the shoebox on top of the second wagon.

"Hello," he said. "Now here's a good idea. Look at this, Sam! These boys have a special pet in reserve. That's what I call smart merchandising!"

Well, of course, everyone crowded around to see what the special pet was; and Bruce, with a silly smile on his dopey face, untied the box and lifted up the lid.

What was in the box was—a rattlesnake.

I guess you can imagine what happened next. All the people shoving and pushing to get away from us got the animals so upset that they began to stampede too. The skunk got crowded into a storefront, and that scared him, and he did what skunks always do when they get scared. There were calves and goats going every which way, and the dogs all went crazy and started chasing anything that ran—and that was everything there was. Our two cages got upset and squashed and all the gophers and white rats went skittering off under people's feet. Wol climbed up on top of my head and kept beating his wings so I couldn't see too much of was happening, but I could still hear it. Women were screaming, and one of the Mounties had hauled out his big revolver and was waving it in the air, while the other one never stopped blowing his silver whistle. All you could hear was yells and howls and barks and screams and yowls. I tell you, there never had been anything like it in Saskatoon for a hundred years.

We didn't stick around any longer than we could help. We saved the wagons, our two dogs, the owls, and that darn snake. Bruce grabbed the shoebox the moment the ruckus started and stuck to it like a bur until we got back to my place.

"Gee," he said, as we were getting a drink from our garden hose. "If I'd lost that old snake I'd have got my britches tanned from here to Mexico. It belongs to our hired man, and it's been his pet for fifteen years—ever since he was a cowboy down in the Cypress Hills. It's so old it hasn't any teeth, nor any poison either, but he sure is fond of it all the same. It sleeps right with him in his bunk. . . ."

I still think we should have won first prize.

Farley Mowat

General Store

Some day I'm going to have a store
With a tinkly bell hung over the door,
With real glass cases and counters wide
And drawers all spilly with things inside.
There'll be a little of everything;
Bolts of calico; balls of string;
Jars of peppermint; tins of tea;
Pots and kettles and crockery;
Seeds in packets; scissors bright;
Kegs of sugar, brown and white;
Apple cider for picnic lunches,
Bananas and rubber boots in bunches.
I'll fix the window and dust each shelf,
And take the money in all myself,
It will be my store and I will say:
"What can I do for you today?"

Rachel Lyman Field

Exploring

"Hurry up, David," said Robbie Wilson. "I'm all ready to go exploring but you are so slow. Can't you eat a little faster?"

"Be patient, Robbie," said Mrs. Wilson. "Your cousin David doesn't gulp his food down like you do. The hills will still be there. And besides, Sheryl hasn't finished her breakfast yet."

"Oh Mom," groaned Robbie. "We don't want to be bothered with a silly girl. She'll only spoil our fun and drag along behind us."

"I'm not a silly girl," said Sheryl. "I won't spoil your fun, and I can keep up with you, too."

"Oh, let her come," said David. "It will be all right, Robbie."

"Stop arguing," said Mrs. Wilson firmly. "Sheryl goes with you, Robbie, or no one goes. I've packed a knapsack with some wieners, buns, matches, and canned drinks. There are also some apples for dessert. You may build a small fire and cook your hot dogs over it. Just be sure you put the fire out."

"Golly, that will be fun," shouted the children.

Soon they were climbing happily over rocks on the hills behind the Wilson farm.

"This is really exciting," grinned David. "We don't have any place like this to explore in the city."

"There are some old mine tunnels over there," said Robbie. "Let's see if we can find one."

Sheryl grabbed her brother's arm. "No, Robbie, Dad said we were never to go near those old mines. They're not safe."

"See," said Robbie to his cousin. "See—I said she'd spoil our fun. Girls are always scared of things."

"Maybe we'd better not go," answered David. "Maybe we'd better do what your dad said."

"You're a chicken, just like Sheryl," yelled Robbie. "Go home if you want to. I'm not scared and I'll go alone."

Robbie started towards the old mining hills. They were covered with bushes, long grass, and weeds. Sheryl and David stood on a rock and watched him go. Slowly David started after Robbie.

"I guess it will be all right," he said. "I'm going too—are you coming?"

Sheryl didn't answer David. She just stood and watched the boys grow smaller and smaller and then disappear into the brush.

Soon David caught up to Robbie. "I'm glad you've changed your mind," said Robbie.

"Let's look over in those bushes against that steep hill."

The boys trudged slowly through the twisted brush.

"There's a mine!" yelled Robbie. "Come on, let's explore it." The boys peered into the entrance of the deserted mine. "Wait," cautioned David. "It's sure dark and scary in there."

Old timbers, dark with age, supported the roof of the entrance.

"Come on, let's see what's inside," urged Robbie, as he started into the black opening in the hillside. David followed close behind. The timbers creaked and groaned as the boys groped through the darkness. Suddenly, Robbie stumbled and and fell against one of the old timbers. A splitting crash echoed through the mine. Falling timber surrounded the boys.

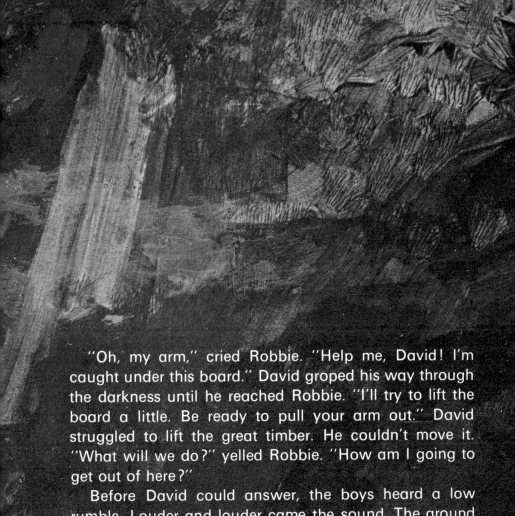

"Oh, my arm," cried Robbie. "Help me, David! I'm caught under this board." David groped his way through the darkness until he reached Robbie. "I'll try to lift the board a little. Be ready to pull your arm out." David struggled to lift the great timber. He couldn't move it. "What will we do?" yelled Robbie. "How am I going to get out of here?"

Before David could answer, the boys heard a low rumble. Louder and louder came the sound. The ground seemed to be shaking all around them.

"The mine must be caving in," screamed Robbie. "What will we do?"

With a thundering crash the old timbers at the entrance of the mine collapsed. The roof of rocks and earth came tumbling down. David huddled close to his trapped cousin. Then all was quiet and very dark.

"Robbie, are you all right?" asked David in a very shaky voice. "Yes," sobbed Robbie. "But how will we get out? I can't move from under this timber and now the opening is blocked. No one will ever find us. I'm

"I'm scared too," said David. "But we'll get out! I'll find a way!"

"I wish we had listened to Sheryl," sobbed Robbie.

"I'm going to crawl over some of those rocks and see if I can find a way out," said David.

"Don't leave me alone," yelled Robbie, "please don't leave me."

"Stop yelling," said David firmly. "I must look for an opening. Maybe I can move some of the rocks."

Slowly David crawled towards the entrance. The sharp rocks tore at his clothes and hands, but he kept going. He pulled and pushed at the rocks. They wouldn't move. Tired and hurt, he began to crawl back to his cousin. Then he thought he heard something. Yes, someone was calling.

"Help," screamed David. "We're trapped in here." A small rock near the top of the pile moved. David could see a spot of light.

"Help," he screamed again. A face appeared in the small opening. It was Sheryl. "Are you in there?" she yelled. "Robbie! David! Are you there?"

"Sheryl, go and get help," yelled David. "Robbie is trapped under a timber, and we can't get him out from under it. Go and get your Dad. Hurry, Sheryl!"

The face disappeared. David crawled back to his cousin.

"Sheryl found us," he said. "She'll bring your father and he'll get us out of here." Robbie sobbed quietly as David sat down beside him.

"We'll have a long wait, so let's have something to eat," he said, as he reached into the knapsack that was still on Robbie's back.

Jean Ellis

Willie's Good Recess

Willoughby Rufus Snow was small and dark and, right now, he was cold and unhappy. He was the smallest boy in the second grade of a big public school. He was the only negro boy and he was the only boy who wasn't enjoying recess.

The second grade, along with three other grades, always had recess in the great big high-ceilinged gym. The gym was awfully big. Bigger than three good-sized barns. It was also cold. Willie Snow, who had left a warm climate only three weeks ago, shivered and felt very cold and lonely indeed.

None of the other children seemed to mind the gym being cold. They liked it because they moved so fast they kept warm anyway. Some played dodge ball, others played bat ball. And at one end of the gym a whole lot of them roller-skated with a loud grinding noise of skates.

Willie watched them from out of one corner. He didn't know how to play dodge ball. He didn't know how to play bat ball, and he didn't even own a pair of roller-skates. Willie shivered and wished he were back home where the sun was warm and the children were his friends.

Finally Willie got so cold that his teeth chattered and he just had to move around to get warm. He walked around the huge gym until he came to the stage at one end. Willie was just going to walk past when he saw the big drum. Sometimes the high school orchestra left their instruments on the stage between rehearsals and this was one of those times.

Willie walked straight up to that drum. It was big and beautiful with School Band painted in red letters on the sides. Willie looked at it and looked at it, and just then Willie's teacher came by. Willie looked up at the teacher and then he looked at the drum. "Please, Miss Carter," Willie said almost without meaning to, "could I play that drum?"

"Yes," said Miss Carter. "If you are very, very careful."

Miss Carter walked on past the stage but Willie didn't see her go. He didn't see anything but that great big beautiful drum that drew him like a magnet. He picked up a drumstick and tapped the drum very lightly. There was a surprised little "boom" like the croak of a bull frog.

Willie beamed. He tapped the drum harder. "Boom!" That was a good sharp boom like the slam of a door. This time Willie really swung the drumstick. BB-OOO-MM. The deep shivery sound rolled and drew like thunder. Willie stopped the noise with his hand, though it sounded wonderful. He held the drumsticks lightly now and tapped, tap-tappa-tap, very gently. The beam on Willie's face grew wider and wider. Tap-tappa-tap very softly. Willie was feeling his way. Tap-tappa-tap. Slowly, gradually the tune came. It was as though the drumsticks were leading and Willie's small swaying body just naturally followed.

The tune unfolded in Willie's mind. He no longer heard the shouts of the other children. He no longer heard the thud of their balls or the whirr of roller-skates. All Willie heard was the tune—a lovely song that his father and his uncle used to sing.

Willie Snow hummed the words to himself and beat the strong familiar tune on the drum. When he got to the chorus Willie had forgotten everything except the big drum and the wonderful rolling sounds that came from it.

Willie wasn't cold any more. Willie wasn't small any more, and he certainly wasn't lonely. Willie was part of a

great big wonderful flood of sound that was coming out of that drum.

When the clanging bell that meant the end of recess finally sounded out over the gym and even over the roll of Willie's drum, he was surprised. He was so surprised that he just stood with a drumstick in each hand while the last rumble of the drum melted away with the clanging of the bell.

Then Willie saw Miss Carter and the other children. They had stopped playing ball. They had stopped roller-skating. They had even stopped shouting and talking. They had all crowded around the edge of the platform and were looking up at Willie. Now all of a sudden they broke into a great noisy burst of applause that was even bigger and noisier than the school bell.

He didn't know what to make of it. He looked at Miss Carter and she was clapping too. Finally she stopped and moved over beside him. "Thank you, Willie," she said. "Thank you very much. We all loved the concert."

Willie gave a little gasp of surprise. They were clapping for him! All those big children, who were used to this big school, were clapping for him and the sounds he brought out of that fine, round drum! They too liked that drum and the good tunes that Father and his uncle used to sing.

Willie stood on one foot and then on the other but he didn't know what to say. "Did you have a good recess?" Miss Carter asked. Willie nodded his head excitely.

"Oh, yes, Miss Carter," he said. "I did."

"So did we all," said Miss Carter. "Thanks to you, Willie."

On the way upstairs Johnny Griswold gave him a little poke. "Say, Willie, how's chances to teach me how to roll that drum?" he asked.

Willie grinned. "Sure thing, Johnny, if you show me how to play dodge ball."

"It's a deal. Tomorrow at recess."

Willie was feeling very good indeed.

Lavinia R. Davis

36

Mulberry Joe

There was once a good man who had a cheerful disposition and that was all he possessed in the whole world except a few sticks of furniture, a cupboard not as full as he could wish, and the clothes on his back—and they were not what they had once been.

"But things might be worse," said he, as he pulled in his belt another hole and tied a bit of string on to the end of a broken bootlace. "I might have had a wooden leg, and if it had taken to warping on a damp day, where should I have been then? Aye, to be sure," said he, "things might be a deal worse than they are, but that's not saying they might not be a deal better if I just sat down to think about them."

So he rested on a stone that happened to be handy and he thought and he thought and very soon he had a fine idea.

"I've got it!" cried he and slapped his leg. "I'll have to earn some money!"

So far, so good, but how was the money to be earned?

He thought a little longer. "I can't dig," said he, "for I haven't a spade, and I can't be a blacksmith because I don't know how. But I know what I can do!" cried he and snapped his fingers. "I can sell pies, that I can, and then I'll make a fortune in no time."

The idea was a good one as far as it went, but it did not go far enough. "Who's going to make the pies for me to sell?" he asked himself.

That was a tough nut to crack! But if you suppose he gave in you are vastly mistaken. He just went on sitting and thinking, and thinking and sitting, and before he had grown tired of doing either he had solved the problem.

"I've got it!" he cried and threw up his cap. "I must get a wife. If I had a wife she'd make pies for me to sell, and if I had pies to sell I'd make a fortune. " 'Tis a grand idea," he said, "and now that I have everything thought out I must see about getting married."

Off he went along the road and there was a girl leaning over a gate.

"Good day," said he.

"Good day," said she.

"Can you bake pies?" he asked, for he did not believe in beating about the bush.

"To be sure I can," said she.

"Then will you marry me?"

"No!" said she.

So that was the end of that.

He went along the road a little further and there was a girl sitting on a stile.

"Good day," said he.

"Good day," said she.

"Will you marry me?" he asked, for he always believed in getting to the point.

"I might," said she and looked him up and down.

"But can you bake pies?"

"Of course not," said she.

So that was the end of that.

"If it wasn't for my cheerful disposition I might be getting downhearted," he thought. "But I'll try again."

And try again he did, and if you'll believe me the very next lassie he met was ready and willing to be his wife and was a rare hand with a rolling pin into the bargain.

Away they went to be married, arm in arm as comfortable as you please, for if he had a cheerful disposition, so had she, and they found each other very agreeable company. And when they came home, the first thing they did was to set out the flour barrel and the baking board.

"Now," said he, "if you'll be baking a pie or two, I'll get to work to sell them and make a fortune."

"All right," said she, tucking up her sleeves out of the way, "but there's a bit of a difficulty. You can make a fortune out of selling pies, but I can't make pies to sell out of nothing. What are we going to put inside them?"

"Now I never thought of that!" said he, and but for his cheerful disposition he might have been quite put out.

"If we lived near the sea we might catch eels," said he.

"If we lived on a hill we might gather bilberries," said she.

They sat down together and thought and thought, for she was as good at thinking as he.

"I can't think of anything but mulberries," said he.

"Mulberries will do very well," said she.

But the only mulberries they could find grew at the top of a very tall tree, far out of reach.

"If I had a ladder I could climb up and gather some," said he.

"If I had a long stick I could knock some of them down," said she.

But as they had neither, they sat down under the tree to wait, for, they said, the mulberries are sure to fall down in time. It was pleasantly warm and there was a fine view and they enjoyed the sunshine and each other's conversation till evening came and enough mulberries were lying on the grass around them to fill their basket. Then they went home to bed, so as to be ready to get up early in the morning to bake the pies.

The dew was hardly dried from the grass next day before the pies were ready to sell. There were three of them, all brown and shiny, and the smell that curled out of the little hole in the top was enough to make anyone's mouth water.

The good man put the pies on a tray and put the tray on his head and set out, and he had not gone far before he met a beggar.

"Good day," said he.

"Good day," said the beggar.

"Would you like a mulberry pie?" asked the good man, for he did not believe in wasting words.

"That I would!" said the beggar and sniffed a hungry sniff.

"Then have you any money to buy one?"

"Not I!" said the beggar and sniffed again.

"I meant to make a fortune selling them," said the good man, "but you can have one for nothing because they smell so good!"

So that was the end of the first pie.

The good man went on a little further and he met a wealthy citizen who had breakfasted so well that he was taking a walk to get an appetite for lunch.

"Good day," said the good man.

"Good day," said the citizen.

"Have you any money?" asked the good man, for he did not see the use of wasting time getting to the point.

"Of course I have," said the wealthy citizen.

"Then will you buy a mulberry pie?"

"Not I!" said the citizen and turned up his nose.

"It's as well I have a cheerful disposition," thought the good man; "If I hadn't I might begin to think I wasn't going to make a fortune after all. As it is," said he, "I think I could put a better face on things if I ate a pie myself, for they smell so very good!"

So that was the end of the second pie.

He went on a little further and whom should he meet but the King himself, sitting on a gate drumming his heels, while all the courtiers were getting in each other's way trying to take a stone out of the shoe of His Majesty's horse.

"Heigh-ho!" sighed the King. "I could have borne it better if it had happened after lunch instead of before it. It would be a fine thing indeed if a King were to die of hunger sitting on a gate!"

Then up came the good man with his pie. " 'Tis only made of mulberries," said he, "but a mulberry pie is better than none, seeing it smells so extra good."

"Only a mulberry pie!" cried the King, and set to work on it at once, though he did not forget to spread his handkerchief over his knees to keep the crumbs from falling on his velvet breeches.

"Only a mulberry pie!" cried he as he popped the last morsel in his mouth and wiped his fingers.

"Only a mulberry pie!" he shouted as he pulled out his purse and tossed it to the good man with all that it contained. "It's the finest pie I ever tasted and I'll have one every day, if you'll be so obliging as to deliver one at the palace at dinner time."

Would the good man be so obliging? That he would.

And did he make his fortune? Of course he did.

And did he and his wife live happily ever after?

What a silly question! Could this be a really, truly fairy tale if it ended in any other way?

Margaret Baker

A Day at the Fair

Anna and Dirk were excited as they rode into Garden Valley with their parents. This was to be their very first fair in Canada.

Father knew all about fairs. It would be like a market day in Alkmaar, he told the family. Alkmaar was the nearest town to their farm in the Netherlands. Often Father had taken many cheeses there, to be sold in the marketplace.

Today they would sell their vegetables as well as the cheeses they had made. The vegetables, scrubbed and clipped of their green leaves, were piled carefully into the truck. There were two tubs of big, round, red cheeses for sale. These cheeses had been dipped in a special red dye and covered with wax to keep them from spoiling.

Tucked under six-year-old Dirk's arm was a potato almost the size of a football! He had found it himself, among the potatoes to be sold. He called it his *groet aardappel*—his big "earth apple".

At the gates to the fair, a red-faced man in a new sombrero came rushing up. "You can't bring your truck in here!" he shouted.

"Where do we put the vegetables we wish to sell?" asked Father.

"What? Don't tell me you brought all that stuff to sell at this fair!"

"Yes, yes," replied Father, glancing about. Not a booth of vegetables could he see. What was the matter?

"This isn't that kind of a fair," said the red-faced man. "This isn't a market fair, my friend. At this fair the vegetables are put on display and judged. No one will expect to buy vegetables here." And he went back to the gates to welcome other people who were going in.

"I have made a mistake in what a Canadian fair means," said Father sadly. "This fair is like a *kermis* in the Netherlands. It has sideshows and rides for children. How could I have made such a foolish mistake?"

"Anybody can make a mistake when he is learning a new language," said Mother, patting Father's arm.

Father looked into the disappointed faces of his children. Then he looked at all the vegetables and the beautiful red cheeses. "Come," he said, "we will display vegetables and cheeses here by the roadside. Someone may want to buy. We don't want to go home yet, do we?"

Such a bustle! Soon the shiny red tomatoes were piled in tiers beside the orange carrots and golden corn. Bright green pea pods in open paper bags sat side by side with the round red cheeses. It wasn't long before the family was seated behind their produce, Dirk with the big potato still under his arm.

The crowds grew larger. The people looked at the family, but they did not stop. They went through the gates and on towards the music of a merry-go-round, and all the noise ahead. Not a vegetable nor a cheese was sold.

The sun grew hot. Anna and Dirk became hotter and more unhappy with every passing minute.

"Moeder, may we go to see the merry-go-round?" asked Anna at last.

Mother sighed as she spoke to Father. "I will let them go. No need for them to be unhappy, too. I do wish we had sold some vegetables so we could let them have a ride."

Father nodded. "Mark well this place, Anna," he said, "so you can return when you are ready. Do not be too long."

The children skipped away, hand in hand — Dirk with the big potato still tucked under his arm.

What a beautiful place this fair was! Red and white
streamers everywhere, and tents with the things called
hot dogs and lemonade! Dirk grew thirsty almost at once,
but his eyes could not grow big enough to see everything
there was to see. Men with loud hoarse voices shouted
and spun their big wheels. Behind them were all the
glorious prizes for spinning the right number. No one
seemed to be getting the prizes, so Dirk and Anna did not
feel too sad about leaving them behind. On they walked,
scuffing the sawdust beneath their feet. They saw the
huge signs of the fat lady, the thin man, and another man
who could swallow a sword right up to its hilt.

Dirk and Anna had been thirsty and wanted lemonade;
they had wanted to spin the wheels; they had wanted to

see a man eat fire and another man swallow a sword—
but all of these things were forgotten when they came to
the merry-go-round. Not only were there prancing horses;
there were other animals to ride on—giraffes, elephants,
tigers, and even a kangaroo with a pocket in which a
child could sit.

"Oh, if I could only ride on that big white horse with the
golden saddle!" sighed Dirk.

"I would choose to ride on the tall giraffe!" interrupted
Anna excitedly. "I would be so high up!"

The sun dipped behind one of the tents. Anna gave a
big sigh. "We must go back to Moeder and Vader now.
Come, Dirk."

With one long last look, they started back.

They walked in the right direction, Anna was sure, but the crowd was thicker now, and they could not see past all the people. So Anna turned and went the other way, and then she became all mixed up. She did not tell Dirk, but after a long time of walking about, he grew cross and tired.

"Where's Vader?" he asked.

"I am not sure," answered Anna, pushing a few strands of hair away from her hot face, "but we will find him, never fear."

Dirk looked up into her frightened face. Then, because he was tired and unhappy, because he had not been able to ride on the merry-go-round, and because he was frightened, too, he forgot that he was six years old. He only remembered that he was in a crowd of strange people in a strange land. Before Anna could stop him, out came a bellow you could not help but hear! When Dirk cried he cried!

The crowd came closer.

"They are lost," said a lady.

"Poor little fellow," said another.

"Look," said an old gentleman. "The little boy has a big potato under his arm. They must belong in the fresh vegetable tent. The judge is looking at potatoes now. We had better get these kids over there."

Before Anna could think of something to say, she and Dirk were led to a tent, with many smiling people following. Inside were more potatoes than Dirk had ever seen. He forgot all about crying and stared and stared. No matter where he looked, he could not find an "earth apple" as big as his own.

"Judge!" called out the old gentleman. "Come over here and take a look at this potato. It's about the size of a football!" He lifted Dirk and his potato up on a table for all to see.

A man with a big white button on one side of his coat came rushing over. "The biggest potato I ever set eyes on!" he cried. "Where did you get it, my boy?"

Dirk looked at the judge from under his long eyelashes, but would not say a word.

"From our potato field at home," spoke up Anna.

"Well, I'll certainly have to give it a prize," said the judge. And he did!

He gave Dirk a new dollar bill.

"Why wasn't your potato on display?" asked a lady.

"Vader did not know it was this kind of a fair," replied Anna. "He thought it was like a market in the Netherlands. We brought our vegetables to sell."

"Now I know where these children are from!" said a man. Anna turned to look. It was the red-faced man in the new sombrero. "Their parents are over by the west gate. I'll take them back."

"Did you say you have vegetables to sell, little girl?" asked the lady. "Why, I need some fresh vegetables. I'll be going home soon and I'll stop and buy some."

"They must be fine vegetables," said the old gentleman. "We've just seen one of them. I need some potatoes. I'll call at the west gate on my way home. Will you wait?"

"Yes, yes," said Anna, smiling. She grasped Dirk's hand as she started to follow the red-faced man in the new sombrero. "We will wait. We have some lovely red cheeses you might like, too!"

Before the sun went down in the Alberta sky that night, every vegetable and every round red cheese had been sold. How the money jingled in Father's pocket!

"Hurry!" said Father at last. "We all want rides on the merry-go-round, don't we?"

Laughing, the family ran over to the merry-go-round. It was lighted up for the evening and was more beautiful than ever. How exciting the music sounded!

Mother rode on a tiger!

Father rode on an elephant!

Anna rode high on the tall giraffe!

And Dirk rode on the prancing horse with the golden saddle!

Then the family had some hot dogs and lemonade and some pink cotton-candy.

Mother said, "Before we go home. I *must* see Dirk riding in the kangaroo's pocket!" Mother and Father and Anna laughed until they had to hold their sides as they watched Dirk's excited face peeking out of the kangaroo's pocket, while the merry-go-round went round and round and round.

"Oh, Dirk!" said Anna, as a very happy family drove home in the moonlight. "Aren't you glad you found that big 'earth apple'? Just think of the fun we would have missed if you hadn't!"

"That was a groet aardappel!" murmured Dirk sleepily from between Father's knees, and his hand closed tight over the new dollar bill in his pocket.

Audrey McKim

Daddy Fell into the pond

Everyone grumbled. The sky was grey.
We had nothing to do and nothing to say.
We were nearing the end of a dismal day,
And there seemed to be nothing beyond,
THEN
Daddy fell into the pond!

And everyone's face grew merry and bright,
And Timothy danced for sheer delight.
"Give me the camera, quick, quick, oh quick!
He's crawling out of the duckweed." CLICK!

Then the gardener suddenly slapped his knee,
And doubled up, shaking silently,
And the ducks all quacked as if they were daft
And it sounded as if the old drake laughed.

O, there wasn't a thing that didn't respond
WHEN
Daddy fell into the pond!

Alfred Noyes

Peter and the Wolf

And now, imagine the scene . . . a house in a large garden, with a wall around it. Outside in the meadow there is a big tree and a pond. Not very far away there is the dark, dark forest.

Early one morning Peter opened the gate and went out into the big green meadow. On a branch of a big tree sat a little bird, Alexei—Peter's friend. "All's quiet," chirped Alexei gaily.

Just then Tanya the duck came waddling round. She was glad to see that Peter had not closed the gate, and decided to take a nice swim in the deep pond in the meadow.

Seeing Tanya, the little bird flew down upon the grass, settled next to her, and shrugged his shoulders. "Huh! What kind of a bird are you if you can't fly?" said he.

To this the duck replied, "What kind of a bird are you if you can't swim? Huh!" and she dived into the pond. They argued and argued, Tanya swimming in the pond and Alexei hopping along the shore.

Suddenly something caught Peter's attention. He noticed Vasily the cat crawling through the grass. Vasily thought, "The bird is busy arguing. I'll just grab him." Stealthily he crept towards Alexei on his velvet paws.

"Oh. Look out!" cried Peter.

And Alexei immediately flew up into the tree while the duck quacked angrily at the cat—from the middle of the pond. Vasily walked round and round the tree and thought, "Hmmm. Is it worth climbing up so high? By the time I get there the bird will have flown away."

Just then Grandfather came out. He was angry because Peter had gone to the meadow. "It's a dangerous place," he said. "If a wolf should come out of the forest, then what would you do?"

Peter paid no attention to Grandfather's words. Boys like him are not afraid of wolves. But Grandfather took Peter by the hand, locked the gate, and led him home.

No sooner had Peter gone than a big grey wolf came out of the forest. In a twinkling Vasily the cat climbed up into the tree. Tanya the duck quacked, and in her great excitement, jumped out of the pond.

No matter how hard Tanya tried to run, she couldn't escape the wolf. He was getting nearer, nearer, nearer, nearer—and then he got her, and with one gulp swallowed her.

And now this is how things stood: Vasily the cat was sitting on one branch, Alexei the bird was sitting on another—not too close to Vasily—and the wolf walked round and round the tree, looking at them with greedy eyes.

In the meantime, Peter, without the slightest fear, stood behind the closed gate, watching all that was going on. He ran into the house, got a strong rope, and climbed up the high stone wall. One of the branches of the tree, round which the wolf was walking, stretched out over the wall. Grabbing hold of the branch, Peter lightly climbed over onto the tree.

Peter said to Alexei, "Fly down and circle around the wolf's head, only take care he doesn't catch you!" Alexei almost touched the wolf's head with his wings, while the wolf snapped angrily at him from this side and that. How the bird worried the wolf! How the wolf wanted to catch him! But Alexei was cleverer, and the wolf simply couldn't do anything about it.

Meanwhile, Peter made a lasso, and carefully letting it down, he caught the wolf by the tail and pulled with all his might. Feeling himself caught, the wolf began to jump wildly, trying to get loose. But Peter tied the other end of the rope to the tree, and the wolf's jumping only made the rope around his tail tighter.

Just then, the hunters came out of the woods, following the wolf's trail, and shooting as they went. But Peter, sitting in the tree, said, "Don't shoot! The bird and I have already caught the wolf. Now help us take him to the zoo."

And there—imagine the triumphant procession! Peter at the head, after him the hunters, leading the wolf, and winding up the procession, Grandfather and the cat. Grandfather shook his head discontentedly. "Well, and if Peter hadn't caught the wolf—what then?" he thought.

Above them flew Alexei the bird, merrily chirping, "What brave fellows we are, Peter and I! Look what we have caught."

And if you would listen very carefully, you would hear the duck quacking away inside the wolf, because in his haste the wolf had swallowed her alive.

Peter Ustinov

69

He Did It

Said the dangerous sea,
"You'll not conquer me,
Try as hard as you can.
You are not a whale,
You are not a shark—
You cannot walk
On the waves, young man."

So he made a boat
That was able to float.
"Ho, ho!" said his foe,
"It floats all right
And it's watertight,
But you can't make it go."
"Oh yes I can,"
Replied the young man.
And he made some oars
And learned how to row.

70

When the sea saw
The boats and the oars
And all the rowers,
He said, "Young man,
They make a fine show,
But what will you do
When they venture out
Where the deep sea swells
Can take them up
And toss them about
Like cockle shells?"
"You can't stump me,"
Said the bright young man,
And cut down a tree
And made a tall mast
And rigged it with sails,
To catch the high winds
And weather the gales.

When the ships set out
With their sails unfurled
To cross the Atlantic
And discover the world,
The sea looked them over
From stern to stem
And when he saw,
With considerable awe,
That Columbus himself
Was on one of them,
He said, with a show
Of humility,
"I admit, young man,
You have conquered me."

Mary Britton Miller

73

Ocean Wonders

Exploring the Ocean

Have you ever dived into the ocean from the end of a pier? Did your lungs feel as if they might burst?

People are not built to live under the water for a long time. We must have air to breathe. But some people can hold their breath much longer than you or I.

In Japan, women who are pearl divers can stay underwater for a long time. When they are children they start training to hold their breath.

It is their job to take care of the oyster beds. When the oysters are young, the pearl divers "plant" a tiny bead under the shell of each one. The bead feels rough to the oyster, and so he "builds" a smooth pearl around it.

After several years, the oyster has built a shining, round pearl, layer upon layer. Then the women dive down and "harvest" the oysters. They open them and take out the pearls. They separate the large pearls from the small ones. The biggest pearls are very valuable. They can be sold for a good price.

Man began to invent new ways for people to stay underwater for a long time without coming up for air. He wanted to go farther from shore, into deeper waters than the pearl divers could. He was sure that there were many ocean wonders that the pearl divers had never seen.

One of the best new inventions was a special helmet for divers. Helmet divers breathe air that flows into their helmets through a long cable connecting the diver to a ship.

The heavy suits that the helmet divers wear keep them warm in the deep, cold water a long way from the shore.

Helmet divers have stayed down long enough to find treasures on sunken ships. They have helped build tunnels. But they could not move about freely. Their air hoses were like leashes, and they could not move very far or very fast in their heavy suits.

Finally, a Frenchman named Jacques Cousteau thought of a way to carry air right into the water with him. He strapped it to his back. He wore goggles over his eyes and flippers on his feet. People called him a "manfish." Cousteau could wriggle into caves and explore. He could swim with a school of fish and take pictures.

Soon there were menfish, and sometimes the menfish met "killers" underwater. They saw *sharks* with knife-sharp teeth, *stingrays*, which can cut a man badly with a flip of their whiplike tails, and *electric eels*, which carry their own batteries and can give a person a bad shock.

Some of the mean-looking animals that the menfish saw were harmless and did not attack them. The huge *manta ray*, the "bat" of the ocean, "flies" out of a man's way. And the soft-bodied *octopus*, with its eight arms, is really very shy. The menfish saw many strange, new creatures, but they still could not dive to the deepest part of the ocean.

It is dangerous to swim under very deep water. Man's body cannot stand all the heavy water pressing down on him. The weight of water can crush a man's body and flatten it.

Have you ever broken a balloon by pressing down on it with all your weight? If you have, you have an idea of what happens to man's body under deep water.

To explore the deepest part of the ocean, man had to learn how to build a "shell". He needed something to protect his brittle bones and his tender insides.

And finally, such a shell was invented by William Beebe, an American. He named it the *bathysphere,* which means "deep-sea ball." The bathysphere could only go down to the end of its cable. But it still went much deeper than anything had before.

Then Auguste Piccard, a Swiss scientist, invented a deep-sea boat, the *bathyscaphe*. It was not attached to a cable and could go straight down to the ocean floor. It took six hours to reach the bottom. The two men who rode in its *gondola,* or cabin, were so cramped that they could hardly move. It was like spending the whole day in a pitch black, freezing cold elevator going down, down, down.

Today there are many kinds of boats that explore the deep blue sea. One of them is *Denise,* invented by Jacques Cousteau, the manfish. She can skim on the surface of the water, stop on a dime, dive way down, shoot up, stand on her nose, and even blow two spouts of water from her head like a whale.

Treasures of the Ocean

The wonder food of the ocean is *plankton.* It is a "soup" of tiny animals and plants, some of which are as small as a speck of dust.

Plankton comes in all shapes: circles, squares, triangles, and spirals. Shrimps eat plankton. Herrings eat plankton. Big blue whales eat plankton. And—someday you may eat plankton! Dried plankton is like flour. One day you may have a meal of plankton bread and plankton burger that will taste like meat. And, of course, there will be plankton cake for dessert.

Someday, plankton farms may be carried on spaceships to help feed the crews.

Plankton rides the highways of the ocean, which we call *currents.* Hungry little fish follow the plankton, and hungry big fish follow the little fish. All of them ride the ocean currents. Fishing boats follow the fish, and they ride the currents, too.

(Courtesy Carolina Biological Supply Company)

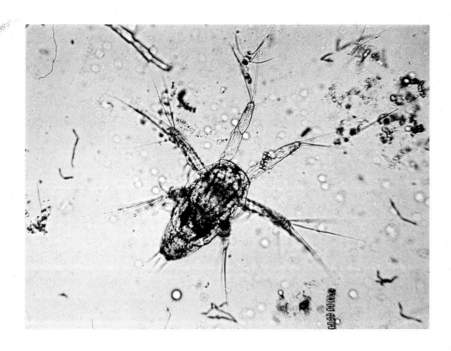

The restless currents carry the waters of the oceans round and round our earth. The great oceans circle our globe with a ring of water that scientists call the *World Ocean*. It covers twice as much space as all the land in every country put together. And the World Ocean is full of treasures, even gold. But the big problem is to get these treasures *out* of the sea. Often it is like trying to get sugar out of a cup of coffee.

Nodules, or lumps of minerals, are scattered over the ocean floor. We could use them, but it is slow work for undersea miners to pick them up.

Scientists believe that the ocean has plenty of "black gold", or oil, too. Oil companies have set up man-made islands on stilts to get this oil. Men drill oil wells beneath the ocean floor, miles from shore.

Each year man is learning to take more treasures from the wonderful world of the ocean. Next time *you* dive off an ocean pier, what ocean wonder will you find?

Eunice and Faith Holsaert

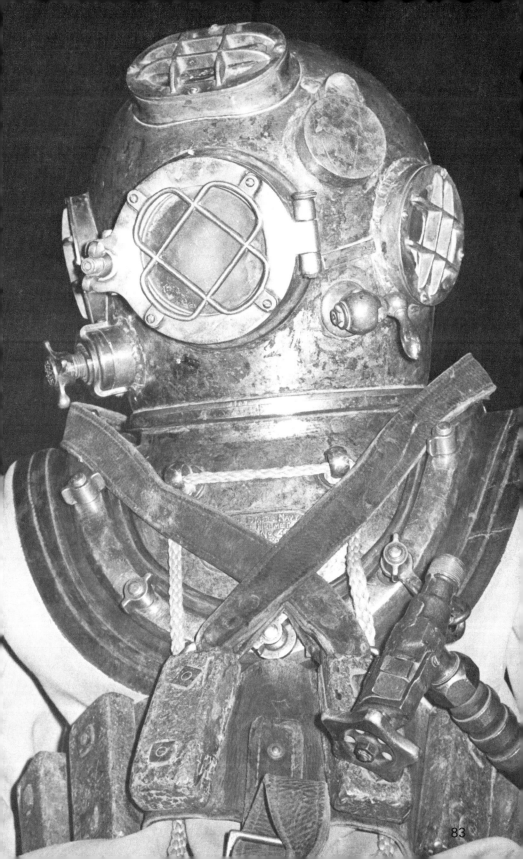

You Are Old, Father William

"You are old, Father William," the young man said,
   "And your hair has become very white;
And yet you incessantly stand on your head—
   Do you think, at your age, it is right?"

"In my youth," Father William replied to his son,
   "I feared it might injure the brain;
But now that I'm perfectly sure I have none,
   Why, I do it again and again."

"You are old," said the youth, "as I mentioned before,
    And grown most uncommonly fat;
Yet you turned a back-somersault in at the door—
    Pray what is the reason of that?"

"In my youth," said the sage, as he shook his grey locks,
    "I kept all my limbs very supple
By the use of this ointment—one shilling the box—
    Allow me to sell you a couple."

"You are old," said the youth, "and your jaws are too weak
    For anything tougher than suet;
Yet you finished the goose, with the bones and the beak;
    Pray, how did you manage to do it?"

"In my youth," said his father, "I took to the law,
    And argued each case with my wife;
And the muscular strength which it gave to my jaw,
    Has lasted the rest of my life."

"You are old," said the youth, "one would hardly suppose
    That your eye was as steady as ever;
Yet you balanced an eel on the end of your nose—
    What made you so awfully clever?"

"I have answered three questions and that is enough,"
    Said his father; "don't give yourself airs!
Do you think I can listen all day to such stuff?
    Be off, or I'll kick you downstairs!"

Lewis Carroll

In the Barbershop

It was very quiet in the barbershop. The barber was shaving an elderly gentleman.

Captain Cook found this spectacle very interesting, and in order to get a better view, he jumped up on the mirror ledge.

"Good night!" said the barber.

The gentleman in the barber's chair, his face already white with lather, half-lifted his head to see what had happened.

"Gook!" said the penguin, flapping his flippers and reaching out his long beak toward the lather on the gentleman's face.

With a yell and a leap, the gentleman rose from his reclining position, left the barber's chair, and fled into the street, not even stopping for his coat and hat.

"Gaw!" said Captain.

"Hey," said the barber to Mr. Popper. "Take that thing out of my shop. This is no zoo. What's the idea?"

"Do you mind if I take him out your back door?" asked
Mr. Popper.

"Any door," said the barber, "as long as it's quick. Now
it's biting the teeth off my combs."

Mr. Popper took Captain Cook in his arms, and amid
cries of "Quork?" "Gawk!" and "Ork!" made his way out
of the shop and its back room and out into an alley.

Captain Cook now discovered his first back stairway.

Mr. Popper discovered that when a penguin has found
steps going up somewhere, it is absolutely impossible to

keep him from climbing them. "All right," said Mr. Popper, panting up the steps behind Captain Cook. "I suppose, being a bird, and one that can't fly, you have to go up in the air somehow, so you like to climb stairs. Well, it's a good thing this building has only three stories. Come on. Let's see what you can do."

Slowly but unwearyingly, Captain Cook lifted one pink foot after another from one step to the next, followed by Mr. Popper at the other end of the clothesline.

At last they came to the top landing.

"Now what?" inquired Mr. Popper of Captain Cook.

Finding there were no more steps to climb, Captain Cook turned around and surveyed the steps that now went down.

Then he raised his flippers and leaned forward.

Mr. Popper, who was still panting for breath, had not supposed the determined bird would plunge so quickly. He should have remembered that penguins will toboggan whenever they get a chance.

Perhaps he had been unwise in tying one end of the clothesline to his own wrist.

At any rate, this time Mr. Popper found himself suddenly sliding, on his own white-clad stomach, down the three flights of steps. This delighted the penguin, who was enjoying his own slide just ahead of Mr. Popper.

When they reached the bottom, Captain Cook was so eager to go up again that Mr. Popper had to call a taxi, to distract him.

"432 Proudfoot Avenue," said Mr. Popper to the driver.

The driver, who was a kind and polite man, did not laugh at his oddly assorted passengers until he had been paid.

"Oh dear!" said Mrs. Popper, when she opened the door to her husband. "You looked so neat and handsome when you started for your walk. And now look at the front of you!"

"I am sorry, my love," said Mr. Popper in a humble tone, "but you can't always tell what a penguin will do next."

So saying, he went to lie down, for he was quite exhausted from all the unusual exercise, while Captain Cook had a shower and took a nap in the icebox.

Richard and Florence Atwater

The South Pole

The world is round, like a giant ball. The world is like a great spaceship going around the sun. It takes 365 days for the world to go around the sun once and come back to where it started. We call that a *year*.

Each day of the year the world also turns. It turns about an imaginary line that we draw straight through the world from top to bottom. We call that imaginary line the *axis*. We call the ends of that line the *poles*.

The North Pole is at the top of the world. The South Pole is at the bottom. The poles are the coldest places in the world. They are places of ice and snow and bitter wind. But otherwise they are not very much alike.

There is no land at the North Pole. There is just an ocean covered with big chunks of floating ice.

But there is land at the South Pole. One of the seven continents of the world is found there. This continent is named Antarctica.

Antarctica is one of the loneliest places in the world. No people have ever lived there, except a few scientists and explorers. There are no cities, no trees, no streams, no grass, no lakes. All there is to see is ice and mountains. Ice a mile thick covers the land.

Antarctica is the coldest place in the world. At the South Pole in the wintertime it gets as cold as 125° below zero. Sometimes the wind blows at two hundred miles an hour. Even a summer day is cold at the South Pole. Why is the South Pole so cold?

The world is warmed by the sun. It is warmest where the sunlight strikes straight on. It is coldest where the light hits at a slant.

Because of the way the world goes around the sun, sunlight always hits the South Pole and the North Pole at a slant. So it must always be cold there. Sunlight comes down straight over the jungles of Africa and South America. It is always hot there.

Even at the South Pole, summer is warmer than winter. But summer at the South Pole comes when we in Canada are having winter. Winter arrives there when we are having summer. The warmest days at the South Pole are in December and January. The coldest ones are in June and July.

This happens because the world tilts to one side as it spins around the sun. For half the year, the northern part of the world is tilted toward the sun. The southern part is tilted away. The north gets more sunshine and enjoys spring and summer. Then it is the south's turn to have the warm weather, and the north has fall and winter.

In September the South Pole begins to tilt toward the sun. By January it faces the sun all day long. There is no darkness at all. Then it starts to tilt away again. By March, sunshine no longer can reach the South Pole.

Soon it is winter there. Winter is a long night that lasts for months. The sun is not seen at the South Pole again until August. But then September comes and it is spring again at the bottom of the world.

Since even summer is cold, the ice never melts at the South Pole. It is a place of frosty whiteness. Ninety percent of all the ice in the world is in Antarctica. If it all ever melted, the oceans would rise two hundred feet. Cities near the shores of the oceans, like Halifax and Vancouver, would be flooded everywhere. But scientists do not believe that will happen.

(Captain Cook's ship, "Resolution")

The sea around Antarctica is full of icebergs. Many smaller pieces of ice also float in the water. It is dangerous for ships to try to go through this icy ocean. In stormy weather ships have been smashed between two big slabs of ice.

The early explorers who sailed toward the South Pole could not get through the ice at all. Captain James Cook, a brave English sailor, was the first who even came close. In 1773 Captain Cook took two small ships far into this ocean of ice.

At that time men thought there might be a warm and pleasant land at the South Pole. Captain Cook's government wanted him to discover that land and make friends with its people. But all that Cook saw was an ocean covered with ice. At last the ice grew so thick that he had to stop sailing south. He turned back.

In 1774 Captain Cook tried again. But still the ice was packed so close that he had to give up. "No man will ever venture farther than I have done," he wrote. "The lands which may lie to the south will never be explored."

Captain Cook was wrong. Less than fifty years later other explorers went to the southern ocean.

Today the South Pole is a busy place. Men arrive there almost every day. Instead of riding on sledges, they come by planes or helicopters. Men live there all year round.

Most of the men who stay there are scientists. There is much for them to study. They learn important things about the weather, about life in cold places, about storms, about ice and snow, and much else. They collect the insects and tiny plants of Antarctica. They study the penguins and seals and other animals.

Antarctica has become a big outdoor scientific laboratory. More than a dozen nations send scientists there. A treaty signed by these countries in 1959 sets Antarctica aside as a place for science. No one "owns" Antarctica. It belongs to all the people of the world.

Lee Sebastian

Your Own Bird Sanctuary

A bird sanctuary of your own? It's easier than you think. All it takes is fresh water, scraps of food and enthusiasm. Birds don't require much care, and once they know they can depend on you for food and water, they will return again and again. If you have trees or shrubs in your backyard, some birds will even build their nests there.

The first thing you need is a birdbath, which should be filled to the top every day with fresh, clean water. If you don't have a birdbath, there's no need to buy one—an empty tin pan can be used instead. Just line the bottom with rocks so that the birds have a rough surface to stand on.

Besides a birdbath, the only other piece of equipment you need is a bird feeder. This is also easy to make.

Start with a large piece of wood, 12 inches by 18 inches or bigger. Nail an edge an inch or more high all the way around it, and bore a few holes in the board to keep water from standing in it. Place it on a pole high enough off the ground so that dogs and cats can't reach it.

You can also make a window feeder from a piece of wood one foot wide and as long as your window sill. Nail an edge around the board, and attach it to your house with two metal brackets.

In a backyard bird sanctuary, squirrels are a special problem. They often come to bird feeders, eat the seeds and frighten the birds away. To protect your feeder from them, don't place it near a tree or other object from which the squirrel could jump. You can also wrap a piece of metal around the post of the feeder to keep squirrels from climbing it. If all else fails, make a dome cover for your feeder with wire which has openings large enough for birds but not for squirrels. If you want to feed the squirrels, just throw some field corn and peanuts on the ground, well away from your bird feeder.

What do you feed birds? One of the easiest things is bread crumbs broken into small pieces, about the size of a man's finger tips. Birds can see them from a long way off and will come to eat. Once a few start coming, others will follow and come back regularly. Robins, sparrows, bluejays, grackles, chickadees, and others like bread crumbs.

Seeds, nuts, and fruit provide a more balanced diet for birds. You can purchase already prepared bags of wild bird seed at many grocery and hardware stores. Most birds that like bread crumbs like seeds, too. Chickadees and nuthatches also like sunflower seeds. These can be mixed with your other seeds, or put on a separate feeder so that the smaller birds can eat undisturbed by the large ones which will come to your big feeder.

Suet (beef fat) and peanut butter are other good foods for birds. In fact, some woodpeckers will come into your yard and eat only these.

You can make a container for suet from wire soap dishes or buy ready-made ones. In any case, containers are necessary. Otherwise, large birds might fly off with big chunks of suet. When you use wire mesh containers, the birds can only peck out small pieces of food and leave the rest for others. Some people fill pine cones with suet or peanut butter and hang them in trees for the birds.

When can you start feeding birds? You can start feeding birds in any month of the year, and birds will enjoy the food you provide for them. Many people like especially to feed birds in the winter, when the ground is frozen and covered with snow. For winter feeding, start around the first of October filling your feeder once or twice a day.

Don't stop putting seeds in your feeder after the first few warm days in the spring. You never know when a late winter storm will come and leave your new friends without any food. But why not continue feeding them throughout the whole year?

After a while, you will come to think of some birds as individuals, each with his own characteristics. It may be the way he cocks his head, the way he twitters when he flies, or anything which sets him apart from the others. You may even find a bird friend who will become almost as tame as a pet.

You can borrow a bird book from the public library. You'll soon know the names of those birds who come regularly—English sparrows, cardinals, bluejays, robins and others. And when a new one comes that you have not seen before, you can quickly find what kind it is. The birds won't care whether you know their names or not, but it adds to the fun to see how many different kinds come to feed in your own sanctuary.

Connie Ewbank

Earthworm

Poor little earthworm
Down in the ground,
Nobody loves you
Or wants you around.

Often you're given
To fishes as bait;
Often you're stepped on,
When you're out too late.

But you, little earthworm,
Keep working away,
Enriching and loosening
The soil where you stay.

Clara G. Cornell

THE GRASSHOPPER

Down

a

deep

well

a

grasshopper

fell.

By kicking about
He thought to get out.
    He might have known better,
    For that got him wetter.
    To kick round and round
    Is the way to get drowned,
        And drowning is what
        I should tell you he got.

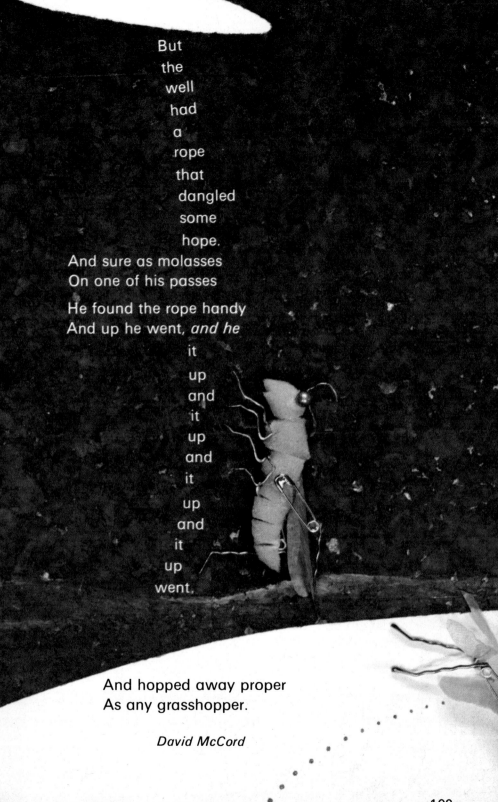

But
the
well
had
a
rope
that
dangled
some
hope.
And sure as molasses
On one of his passes

He found the rope handy
And up he went, *and he*
it
up
and
it
up
and
it
up
and
it
up
went,

And hopped away proper
As any grasshopper.

David McCord

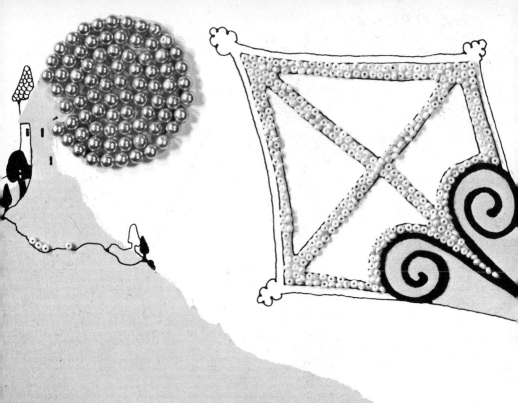

Arturo the Magician

Arturo the Magnificent was a magician, but not an ordinary magician. His tricks were unbelievable.

When he waved white handkerchiefs, they became coloured kites. When he passed his hand over water, it turned into ice. Pumpkins became pies. Bubbles exploded into hundreds of bright feathers. When he threw his cane into the air, it disappeared and a rubber ball fell in its place. It bounced high, but did not fall again. Instead a long coloured ribbon floated down. When it touched the ground, *poof;* there was Arturo's cane!

People came from everywhere to see his tricks. The more they saw of them, the more they wondered how the tricks were done. People begged him to tell his secrets, but he would tell no one, not even his wife.

"Someday," said Arturo, "I will teach our son how to do the tricks my father told only to me."

In less than a year Arturo and his wife were happy to have a son. They called him Ariel.

Ariel grew into a fine young boy. He watched his father perform his tricks hundreds of times. He never tired of seeing them, but he grew more curious and excited as time went on. When Arturo told Ariel that he too would be able to do the tricks one day, Ariel could hardly believe it. Being a magician's son was one thing, but to be a magician himself would be *quite* another.

The day finally came. Arturo whispered to Ariel, "Come with me. I will show you my tricks."

When no one was looking, they stole into an empty room. Ariel barred the door while Arturo locked the windows . . . When they came out it was many hours later.

Ariel couldn't wait to try his first trick. When his father gave him a handkerchief, he flashed it through the air. But there was no coloured kite . . . He hurriedly tried again, but still, nothing happened. Ariel looked at his father. "I can't understand why it doesn't work."

"Try another day. You'll get on to that one later," Arturo said.

Arturo placed a bowl of water before Ariel. Ariel stood ready. He passed his hand over it . . . but there was no ice. Ariel took a deep breath. Remembering that he was trying to be a magician, he passed his hand over it again . . . but the ice trick didn't work.

He attempted other tricks, but pumpkins were still pumpkins and bubbles only broke. When he threw Arturo's cane into the air, it fell to the ground. Each trick failed.

His father was disappointed, but Ariel was heartbroken.

"Will I ever learn magic?" Ariel sadly asked his father.

"You were learning tricks, not magic. It's only magic to people who don't know how they are done," Arturo replied.

Ariel did not understand. "Then what is magic?" he asked.

"Magic is different things to different people. Perhaps when you find what magic is for you, you will be able to do the tricks."

"But where is magic?" Ariel asked.

Arturo thought for a moment, then replied, "Only you can answer that."

Ariel thought about magic and tricks. He wanted to be a magician, but tricks were not magic, and magic was not a trick. Not only could he not do tricks, but he didn't know what magic was—let alone where to find it! The more he thought about it, the sadder and more confused he became. His father and mother tried to cheer him, but he could not be happy.

Ariel spent the summer trying to find magic. When he wasn't trying to find magic, he went to the hills. Day after day he sat in the long grass watching the birds circle in the sky, or the butterflies as they fluttered in the wind. Sometimes he watched the bees as they flew from flower to flower. Most of the time he thought about magic.

One day, as he watched the grass blowing in the wind, he noticed a cocoon that a caterpillar had wrapped himself in. It moved. When he looked more closely, it began to break open. Suddenly, the case was broken, a butterfly appeared, then spread its wings—like magic.

"Magic!" Ariel said aloud, "of course!"

He ran from the hills, back to his home.

"Father! Mother!" he cried, "Come with me!"

His parents saw how excited he was, but wondered what was going on.

He took them to the hills and showed them the birds in the trees, the bees in the flowers, the butterflies, the grass and the sunny rows of corn blowing in the wind.

"Magic was all around me and I didn't know it," Ariel said.

Arturo smiled at his son and said: "It's magic, but no trick."

Ariel was ready to try his father's tricks again. When he did, he found that he could do them all, for he knew the difference between magic and tricks. He amazed everyone who saw him and though he was asked how they were done, he would tell no one; that is, no one but his own son.

Most of Ariel's time was spent in the hills. At home he grew flowers and plants, and built beehives and birdhouses. His garden, in time, became as beautiful as the hills ... And caterpillars changed to butterflies, pollen became honey, and seeds became flowers, fruits or vegetables.

Ariel liked doing tricks; but they were only tricks and did not compare to *his* kind of magic.

David J. Kerr

127

The Chinese Knew

The people living in China thousands
of years ago thought of and used
many things that made their work
easier. They also made things that helped
to make their lives more enjoyable,
They were the first ones to make a wheelbarrow.
They invented block printing.
They discovered how to make porcelain.
They were the first ones to use puppets in shadow play.
The Chinese also knew
how to make a compass,
how to make ink,
how to make an abacus.
how to make and fly a kite!
In this story you will find out
about some of these interesting things
that were known to the Chinese people.
You will understand these better by making some things
that are like those that the Chinese made.

The Chinese knew
how to make kites and fly them in the wind.
They used paper and bamboo sticks to make
their kites. They made them into
shapes of birds, butterflies, fish, stars, and dragons.
They painted them.
They flew these colourful kites
at festival time.
Some of the kites were so huge that
it took many men to fly one of them.

You
can make and fly your own kite.
Put a short thin strip of light wood
across the upper part of a longer
strip, and tie them together
where they cross.
Connect the four ends of the sticks
with a string.
Lay this frame on a large piece
of wrapping paper.
Cut the paper around the frame.
Paste the edges of the paper
around the string. Attach
a narrow strip of cloth
to the bottom of the kite.
Tie a long string to the kite
where the strips cross.
Fly your kite in the wind!

Today
we, too, make and fly kites.
People in some parts of the world
hold kite-flying contests.
Children in many lands throughout
the world have fun flying kites.

The Chinese knew
how to make porcelain.
They mixed and ground a white clay
called *kaolin* with sand and powdered rock.
They washed the mixture several times
and made a thick smooth paste.
They shaped this paste
into vases, bowls, dishes, and jars, and painted them.
The Chinese potters then baked these pieces in a very
hot oven for several days to harden them. They then
allowed the porcelain pieces to cool very slowly.
This porcelain, called "china," became known all
over the world because of its thinness
and its beautiful designs and colours.

Today
porcelain dishes, vases, and figures are still made
by shaping clay and baking it in very hot
ovens, called kilns.
Many of these pieces are made by hand. However,
most of them are shaped by machines and baked
in huge kilns in factories.

You
can make a piece of pottery.
Buy some modeling clay in a store that sells toys.
Shape the clay into a bowl or a dish
and bake it in a kiln to harden it.
If you cannot get the use of a kiln,
let your pottery dry and harden in the air.
Then you can paint and shellac
your bowl or dish.
You have not made a porcelain piece because
it is too difficult for you to make one.
But!
You have found out how to shape
clay and how to harden it.

The Chinese knew
how to make musical instruments.
They hollowed out wood
and made a stringed instrument
called a lute. They plucked the silken strings to get
musical sounds.
They cut short bamboo tubes and made a wind
instrument called a *sheng*. They blew into these tubes
to play tunes.
They made wood and metal drums, gongs,
and bells of many sizes and shapes. The Chinese
struck these instruments to get other musical sounds.
They played these instruments at their festivals
and entertainments.

Today
we make stringed instruments such as banjos,
violins, cellos.
We make wind instruments such as trumpets,
clarinets, saxophones.
We make striking instruments such as drums,
bells, cymbals.
People enjoy listening to the music
when these instruments are played.

You
can make your own toy musical instruments.
Stretch rubber bands of different thicknesses around
an open box. Pluck the bands. Listen to the sound.
Blow across the tops of empty bottles.
Listen to these sounds.
Make drums out of boxes and tin cans of different sizes.
Strike these drums. Listen to the different sounds.
Have fun with these instruments!
Make up a band!

The Chinese knew
how to use a counting frame.
They called it a *suan pan*. We call it
an abacus (ab-uh-kus).
The Chinese made their *suan pan*
by stringing hollow beads on thin bamboo
sticks or on metal rods in a frame.
They moved the beads to figure out the
answers to arithmetic problems.

Today
teachers use bead-frames in classrooms
to teach young children
how to find answers in number work.
Office workers and storekeepers use special machines
to help them work the answers to number problems.
These machines add, subtract,
multiply, and divide numbers very easily.
All the workers have to do is to learn how to press down
the right buttons on the machine
to get the right answers.

You
can make your own counting frame.
Get a heavy cardboard, twelve inches
by fifteen inches in size.
Measure off then dots, one inch apart,
at each of the twelve-inch sides and punch
holes where the dots are.
String then small beads on a cord. Stretch the cord from
one side to the opposite side,
putting each end of the cord
through the hole. Tie knots on the string
in back of each hole so that the line
of beads is fastened straight across.
Make ten lines of beads.

You can learn how to use your counting
frame to help you add, subtract,
multiply and divide numbers.
Your teacher will help you.

The Chinese knew
how to make paper like the kind we use today.
They were the first ones to do so.
They shredded rags, rope, bark of trees, and old
fishing nets, and soaked them in water. They added
glue or starch and pressed the mixture
into very thin sheets. When the sheets dried,
the Chinese had paper.
They used this paper in their writing and drawing.
The Chinese also made wrapping paper,
paper napkins, and wallpaper.

Today
many kinds of paper are made in large mills.
Some paper is made from rags.
Most paper is made from wood pulp.
To make wood pulp, logs are ground into tiny pieces
by machines.
Water and chemicals are added.
The mixture called pulp is then pressed
through different kinds of huge rollers to make paper.

You
can make a simple rag paper.
Cut a piece of old linen cloth into small pieces,
pull the pieces apart, and make a pile of threads. Ask
Mother to help you boil these threads in water for about
ten minutes.
Now, add one-half of a glass of liquid starch. Boil the
mixture for another few minutes. After the mixture cools,
pour it through a piece of wire screen, over the sink.
Try to spread the mixture evenly on the screen.
Place the screen with the threads on it between two
pieces of cloth, and press out the water with a rolling
pin.
Remove the cloth.
You have made paper.

Let it dry overnight.
Take it off the screen slowly
so that it does not tear.
Write on it!

The Chinese knew
how to make ink.
They held iron pot-covers over the flames of lighted
Lampwicks to collect the soot called lampblack. In the
same way, they also collected the soot
of burning pine wood.
They scraped off the lampblack, and mixed it with gum
(a tree sap) until the mixture became a paste.
They added water to the paste and stirred it well.
water to the paste and stirred it well.
This made ink which the Chinese used in their
writing, drawing, and block printing.

Today
many kinds and colours of ink are made by mixing
fine powders or lampblack with oil and chemicals.
These inks are used in writing, printing, copying,
marking, drawing, and stamping.

You
can make your own ink.
Hold a plate over a candle flame for
a short time and then put out the flame.
The black spot that you see on the
plate is lampblack.
Add two or three drops of cooking oil
or machine oil to this lampblack.
Mix it well.
You have made lampblack ink
You can write or draw with this ink.

The Chinese knew
how to do block printing. They invented this
type of printing more than a thousand years ago.
The Chinese wrote words on a large block
of wood. Then they cut away some of the wood
leaving the words raised on the block.
They brushed ink on the words and pressed
a sheet of paper over them. This is how
the Chinese made a page of print.
They were the first ones to print books.
They also printed the first paper money
known in the world.

Today
we block-print designs on wallpaper, draperies, curtains,
tablecloths, and bedspreads by hand and by machine.
We print words on paper with printing presses
using raised letters made of metal. In this way,
we get newspapers, books, and magazines.

You
can make your own block print.
Cut a raw potato into halves.
Draw a triangle on the flat end
of one of the halves. Cut away the potato
around the triangle, leaving the triangle raised.
Press the triangle on an inked
stamping pad or brush ink
or paint on the triangle.
Stamp the design on paper.
You have made a block print.
You can make block prints
of different designs and
of different colours.

The Chinese knew
how to make a compass.
Old Chinese books tell us that the Chinese
had magnet stones, which we call "lodestones." They
placed a pointed lodestone on a piece of wood floating
in water. When the floating wood stopped moving, the
stone always pointed north and south. This was a
compass.
The Chinese used the south-pointing end of the stone
as their guide to find direction.

Today
we use magnetized needles, not lodestones,
in our compasses.
We use the north-pointing end as our guide.
Ship captains, airplane pilots, and scouts use
compasses to help them find direction.

You
can make your own compass.
Magnetize a steel needle by rubbing it many times
on one end of a magnet, one way only.
Fasten the needle through a small piece
of paper. Attach a thread to the edge of the paper
so that the needle hangs straight across.
Tie the other end of the thread to a small flat stick.
Hang the needle inside a glass jar with the stick resting
across the top of the jar. Make sure
that the paper does not touch the jar.
When the needle stops moving, one end will point
toward the north.
Colour this end. It will always point north.
Now find the other directions.
Face toward the north.

East is to your right.
West is to your left.
South is in back of you.
You can use your compass
in the house, on the street,
in the park, to help you
find direction.

The Chinese knew
how to build ships that could stay afloat
even if water leaked through.
They were the first people to build several rows
of wooden walls inside the ship from side to side. If any
water leaked into any section of the ship,
the walls would keep the water
from flowing into the rest of the ship.
The ship would remain afloat!

Today
we build watertight sections in the hulls
of ocean liners, freighters, and submarines.
If the ship is damaged and water is leaking
into it, doors are closed tightly and
the water is kept in the leaking section.

You
can show that watertight sections
will help ships float in water.
Tie together two empty milk cartons, side by side.
You have made a two-section "ship".
Close both covers of the cartons and place
your ship in a tub of water.
Watch your ship float! The air in the watertight
"sections" helps to keep it from sinking.
Now open one cover and let that carton fill with water.
Watch how your ship still floats! The air
in the watertight section helps to keep
the ship from sinking.
Open the other carton and let it fill with water, too.
Watch your ship sink!
Is it not amazing that so long ago, the Chinese knew
and did so many important things?

And
as people in other parts of the world learned about
these things, they, too, began to make and use them.
When they learned how to make wheelbarrows,
they used them to make their work easier.
When they learned how to print books, they
used them to make their lives more interesting.
Look around you!
You will see that we, too, have found ways
of making our work easier
and our lives more enjoyable.

Tilly S. Pine and Joseph Levine

Forty-Seven Wonderful Rockets

When Wan-Hoo walked through the streets of the village wearing his scarlet jacket and carrying his favourite cat under his arm, the people looked up from their work and shook their heads in dismay.

"There goes Wan-Hoo," they whispered to one another. "He is the richest man in the village and surely the most foolish!"

If Wan-Hoo heard them, he gave no sign. He merely walked along, looking at the sky and tickling his favourite cat under the chin.

"Wan-Hoo wants to fly to the stars," they said in the village. "He wants to soar like a kite."

But Wan-Hoo gave no sign that he had heard. He went his way, carrying his favourite cat and looking at the sky.

When he was outside the village, walking along the road, he nodded his head once or twice. Then he scratched his favourite cat behind the ears.

"It is possible," he said. "It is indeed possible. For who is to say what is possible and what is not?"

His favourite cat, Ching, purred agreement and looked at Wan-Hoo with green cat eyes.

"There are those who say that all things are possible," said Wan-Hoo. "And if that is so, then this is indeed possible."

Ching licked absently at Wan-Hoo's fingers, swished his tail once, and closed his eyes.

"Kites soar in the air," said Wan-Hoo. "There is no reason why a kite could not be large enough to carry a man with it. I am certain it is possible." He prodded Ching in the ribs so that the big cat opened his sleepy eyes. "The kite may even be large enough to carry a man and a cat," promised Wan-Hoo.

Wan-Hoo hurried back to his home, walking so quickly that the coattails of his red jacket flapped behind him.

"There goes Wan-Hoo again," whispered the villagers. "Who knows what nonsense he is dreaming now?"

But Wan-Hoo gave no sign that he had heard. He rushed into his house and gave orders that five large kites be made.

"Kites larger than any you have ever seen," said Wan-Hoo firmly. "Kites large enough to carry a man."

In his arms, Ching stirred and twitched his tail.

"Kites large enough for a man and a cat," said Wan-Hoo.

When they were ready, ten servants carried the five kites to a field outside the village and waited for Wan-Hoo to join them.

Finally, dressed in a purple jacket embroidered with gold thread, and carrying Ching carefully under his arm,

Wan-Hoo walked through the streets of the village.

"The richest man in the village and surely the most foolish," whispered the villagers one to another as he passed by.

But Wan-Hoo gave no sign that he had heard. He tickled Ching behind the ears and straightened the purple satin ribbon around his neck and kept right on walking.

As he passed, the villagers stopped their work and trailed along behind him, so that by the time they reached the field where the ten servants waited with the five kites, a long procession wound along the road.

"What possesses Wan-Hoo?" asked the villagers. "Why does he want to sail into the sky?"

"Who can tell the workings of the mind of such a man?" asked the oldest man in the village. "It is not for us to know."

But one very small boy, younger and bolder than the others, hurried up to Wan-Hoo.

"Why do you want to sail into the sky?"

Wan-Hoo looked surprised. "Why, because it has never been done before," he said. "That is reason enough."

He looked around at the crowd, nodded his head politely, and scratched Ching behind the ears. Then he waved his hand and the ten servants rushed forward to strap the kites to him.

When all the ropes were secured, Wan-Hoo waved his hand again, and the servants released the kites. The people from the village gasped and clung to one another

and cried out that something dreadful was sure to happen.

Slowly the five kites rose into the air, with Wan-Hoo and Ching, his favourite cat, held firmly by the rope harness.

Wan-Hoo looked down into the faces of the villagers and smiled and waved. The five kites floated over a treetop, and Wan-Hoo nodded his head to a nesting bird.

Then the kites floated towards a larger group of trees, and before Wan-Hoo knew what was happening, the ropes became entangled and the strong paper of the kites crumpled against the branches.

Wan-Hoo, with Ching still tucked under his arm, climbed down from the tallest of the trees without saying a word to anyone. As he passed his ten servants, he clapped his hands twice and motioned for them to retrieve the remains of the kites.

Then he walked silently back through the village to his home.

As he went inside and closed the door behind him, he said to Ching, "We sailed a little distance into the sky, and that is something that surely has never been done before. And, if we can sail a little way, surely we can sail a long way." He tickled Ching behind the ears. "We will have to think about this."

For many days after that, Wan-Hoo, with his favourite cat under his arm, walked up and down the streets of the village, glancing neither to the right nor to the left.

"He is pondering his foolishness," declared some of the villagers. "Now, surely, he must realize that it is unwise to sail into the skies."

"He has eaten nothing for three days," reported his servants. "He is so deep in thought he does not even sleep."

One morning, Wan-Hoo did not appear in the streets of the village, and the people nodded their heads in satisfaction.

"Wan-Hoo is content now to stay home and tend to gentlemanly pursuits," said the villagers. "He will talk no more of sailing into the sky on five giant kites."

But when his servants came into the village, they spoke in worried voices.

"He is more determined than ever to sail into the air," they reported. "He is sending us throughout the entire country to gather together the largest rockets we can find. He says that rockets will take him into the sky."

The villagers shook their heads. "Rockets are for national holidays and name days," they said. "They are not carrying Wan-Hoo into the air!"

But the servants sighed and held up the money bags they carried. "Wan-Hoo has ordered us to search for rockets," they said. "We must do as he has commanded."

The days went by and Wan-Hoo remained in his house, talking to Ching and planning what to do with the many large rockets he had sent his servants to find.

"I will order the servants to build a large framework," said Wan-Hoo. "Large enough to carry a man. And a cat. And I will order the servants to attach the many large rockets to the framework." He smiled. "That will carry us into space, Ching."

When the servants had searched the country, they returned, piling the many large rockets on the floor in front of Wan-Hoo.

"Forty-seven wonderfully large rockets," said Wan-Hoo, counting them. "Surely enough to carry a man—and a cat—into the air."

"Carry you into the air, they may," said the oldest servant of all. "But carry you where?"

Wan-Hoo looked thoughtful. "Is that important?" he said finally. "Surely what is important is—is it possible?"

When all was ready, Wan-Hoo ordered forty-seven servants to carry the forty-seven rockets. They walked through the village, followed by Wan-Hoo himself, wearing an emerald green jacket with silver embroidery and carrying his favourite cat under his arm.

Once again the villagers left their work and trailed along behind, so that the procession wound through the streets, along the road, out to the field.

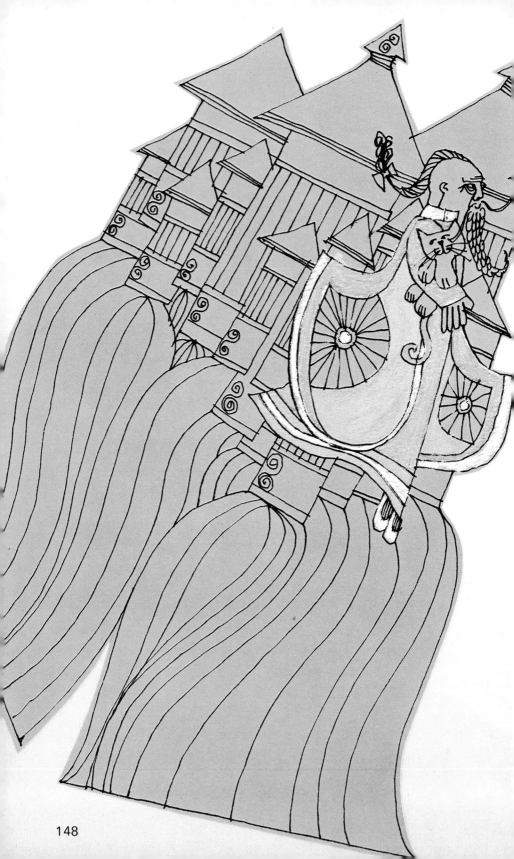

Under the direction of Wan-Hoo, the forty-seven servants attached the forty-seven rockets to the framework. When all was in readiness, Wan-Hoo seated himself in the very centre of the framework. He tickled Ching under the ears and smiled around at the villagers. Then he nodded very politely.

He clapped his hands as a signal for the forty-seven servants to light the forty-seven rockets.

They hesitated, and Wan-Hoo clapped his hands again.

The forty-seven servants hurried forward then and lit the rockets as they had been commanded to do.

A mighty roar filled the air, a cloud of ink-black smoke billowed forth, and flames shot skyward.

The servants and the villagers fell to their knees, faces buried in their hands, crying that Wan-Hoo had aroused the anger of the gods with his forty-seven rockets.

When all was quiet again and the smoke and flame had died away, the villagers and the forty-seven servants slowly raised themselves and looked up at the sky. Then they searched the field. There was no trace of Wan-Hoo above or below.

"The gods have destroyed him," insisted the people of the village. "Wan-Hoo and his favourite cat and his forty-seven rockets have been turned to ashes!"

But the oldest, wisest man in all the village shook his head and said, "It is not for us to know what happened to Wan-Hoo."

"But he has gone," insisted the villagers. "He is no longer here!"

He is only gone from here," said the oldest, wisest man in all the village. "That is not to say that he is not someplace else." He stared up at the sky. "Who among us can say that Wan-Hoo and his favourite cat are not sailing through the sky with the forty-seven wonderful rockets? Who is to say where Wan-Hoo is?"

And the villagers and the servants raised their heads and stared skyward.

"There are those who say that all things are possible," they said to one another. "And if that is so, then this is perhaps possible. And who is to say that the flash of a comet may not be the flap of Wan-Hoo's coat-tails?"

And from time to time, when a puff of smoke powdered the sky, or a streak of emerald green startled the night, the villagers smiled and said, "Surely it is true that all things are possible."

Lorrie McLaughlin

151

A
Coffeepot
Face

I saw
my face
in the coffeepot.
Imagine,
a coffeepot face!

My cheeks
were big
and my nose was not,
and my mouth
was every place.

Aileen Fisher

153

The
Jackal
and the
Alligatr

Once there was a little Jackal who was very fond of shellfish. He used to go down by the river and hunt along the edges for crabs and such things. And once, when he was hunting for crabs, he was so hungry that he did something that he should never have done. He put his paw into the water after a crab without first looking. The minute he put in his paw, snap!—the big Alligator who lived in the mud had the Jackal's paw in his jaw.

"Oh dear!" thought the little Jackal, "the big Alligator has my paw in his mouth! In another minute he will pull me down and gobble me up! What shall I do? What shall I do?" Then suddenly he thought, "I'll deceive him!"

So in a very cheerful voice, as if nothing at all were the matter, he said, "Ho! ho! Clever Mr. Alligator! Smart Mr. Alligator, to bite that old bulrush root thinking it was my paw! I hope you'll find it very tender!"

The old Alligator was hidden away beneath the mud and bulrush leaves, and he couldn't see anything. He thought, "Oh dear! I've made a mistake." So he opened his mouth and let the little Jackal go.

The little Jackal ran away as fast as he could, and as he ran he called out, "Thank you, Mr. Alligator! Kind Mr. Alligator! So kind of you to let me go!"

The old Alligator lashed with his tail and snapped with his jaws, but it was too late; the little Jackal was out of reach.

For some time the little Jackal kept away from the
river, out of danger. But after about a week he got such
an appetite for crabs that nothing else would satisfy
him. He felt that he must have a crab. So he went down
by the river and looked all around, very carefully. He
didn't see the old Alligator, but he thought to himself,
"I'll not take any chances." So he stood still and began
to talk out loud to himself. He said, "When I don't see
any little crabs on the land I usually see them sticking
out of the water, and then I put my paw in and catch
them. I wonder if there are any fat little crabs in the
water to-day?"

The old Alligator was hidden down in the mud at the bottom of the river. When he heard what the little Jackal said, he thought, "Aha! I'll pretend to be a little crab, and when he puts his paw in, I'll have him for my dinner." So he stuck the black end of his snout above the water and waited.

The little Jackal took one look, and then he said, "Thank you, Mr. Alligator! Kind Mr. Alligator! You are exceedingly kind to show me where you are! I will have dinner elsewhere." And he ran away like the wind.

The old Alligator was so angry that he foamed at the mouth, but the little Jackal was gone.

For two whole weeks the little Jackal kept away from the river. Then one day he got a feeling inside him that nothing but crabs could satisfy: he felt that he must have at least one crab. Very cautiously, he went down to the river and looked all around. He saw no sign of the old Alligator. Still, he did not intend to take any chances. So he stood quite still and began to talk to himself. It was a little way he had. He said, "When I don't see any little crabs on the shore, or sticking up out of the water, I usually see them blowing bubbles from under the water. The little bubbles go puff, puff, puff, and then they go pop, pop, pop. They show me where the little juicy crabs are, so I can put my paw in and catch them. I wonder if I shall see any little bubbles to-day?"

The old Alligator, lying low in the mud and weeds, heard this, and he thought, "Pooh! That's easy enough. I'll just blow some little crab-bubbles, and then he will put his paw in where I can grab it."

So he blew, and he blew, a mighty blast. Bubbles rose in a perfect whirlpool, fizzing and swirling.

The little Jackal didn't have to be told who was underneath those bubbles: he took one quick look, and off he ran. As he ran, he sang, "Thank you, Mr. Alligator! Kind Mr. Alligator! You are the kindest Alligator in the world, to show me where you are! I'll have breakfast at another part of the river."

The Old Alligator was so furious that he crawled up on the bank and went after the little Jackal. But he couldn't catch the little Jackal because he ran far too fast.

After this, the little Jackal did not like to risk going near the water, so he ate no more crabs. Instead he ate figs which he found growing in a garden. They were so good that he went there every day and ate them instead of shellfish.

When the old Alligator found this out, he made up his mind to have the little Jackal for supper. So he crept, and crawled, and dragged himself over the ground to the garden. There he made a huge pile of figs under the biggest of the wild fig trees, and hid himself in the pile.

After a while the little Jackal came dancing into the garden, very happy and carefree—but looking all around. He saw the huge pile of figs under the big fig tree.

"H-m", he thought, "that looks very much like my friend, the Alligator. I'll investigate a bit."

He stood quite still and began to talk to himself—it was a little way he had. He said, "The little figs I like best are the fat, ripe, juicy ones that drop off when the breeze blows. Then the wind blows them about on the ground. That great heap of figs over there is so still that I think they must all be dried up."

The old Alligator, underneath the fig pile, thought, "Oh bother, that suspicious little Jackal! I shall have to make these figs roll about, so that he will think the wind is moving them." So he humped himself up and moved about until his back showed through the pile of figs.

The little Jackal did not wait for a second look. He ran out of the garden as fast as the wind. But as he ran he called back, "Thank you again, Mr. Alligator; very sweet of you to show me where you are. I can't stay to thank you as I should like. Good-bye!"

At this the old Alligator was furious. He vowed that he would have the little Jackal for supper this time. So he crept and crawled over the ground till he came to the little Jackal's house. Then he crept and crawled inside, and hid himself there in the house, to wait till the little Jackal came home.

By and by the little Jackal came dancing home, happy and carefree, but looking all around. As he came along, he saw that the ground was all scratched up as if something very heavy had been dragged over it. The little Jackal stopped and looked.

"What's this? what's this?" he said.

Then he saw that the door of his house was crushed at the sides and broken, as if something very big had gone through it.

"What's this? what's this?" the little Jackal said. "I think I'll investigate a little!"

So he stood quite still and began to talk to himself (you remember, it was a little way he had). He said, "How strange that my little House doesn't speak to me! Why don't you speak to me, little House? You always speak to me, if everything is all right. I wonder if anything is wrong with my little House?"

The old Alligator thought to himself that he must certainly pretend to be the little House, or the little Jackal would never come in.

"Hullo, little Jackal!" said the old Alligator in his most pleasant voice.

Oh! When the little Jackal heard that, he was terrified.

"It's the old Alligator," he whispered, "and if I don't make an end of him this time he will certainly make an end of me. What shall I do?"

He thought very quickly. Then he spoke out pleasantly.

"Thank you, little House, it's good to hear your pretty voice, and I will be in soon. First I must gather some firewood for dinner."

He went and gathered a great deal of firewood and piled it up against the door. He lit the firewood and waited.

Soon he had smoked that old alligator right out of the house.

Mary Frere

161

Allin Grows Up

Allin Alligator swam slowly through the hot steamy swamp. His strong tail propelled him smoothly among the plants and weeds. Allin was very happy. Today was his birthday. Allin was one year old. He was two feet long and weighed ten ounces. "Now I'm big enough to explore this lovely swamp," thought Allin. "I'm big enough to find my own home and look after myself."

A year ago Allin's mother had built a large nest on the ground near the water. She had made the nest from grass weeds, sticks and mud. It had been a very big nest. When it was completed, she had laid about twenty-five eggs. The eggs were like large hen eggs. Allin's mother had covered the eggs with rotten leaves, grass and mud. She had stayed nearby to protect her nest from egg-eating animals. The hot sun and the heat from the rotting plants and grasses had hatched the eggs. In eight weeks the shells began to crack and Allin and his many brothers and sisters wiggled out of the shells. Mother Alligator tore away the leaves and grass and mud to release her babies from the nest. Allin was nine inches long and only weighed two ounces. Allin's mother took her family to a safe place. She caught fish for them to eat. Some large fish, herons, and other water birds eat baby alligators. Sometimes even old and very hungry alligators eat the babies. Mother always tried to protect them from their many enemies. She was a very good mother.

Suddenly, a loud shot shattered the peaceful stillness of the swamp. Quickly Allin Alligator dived to the bottom of the pond. Then he floated towards the surface under some water plants. Just his eyes and nostrils were out of the water. He was safely hidden. Allin saw two men in a boat. They were carrying rifles and were searching the water. Allin was puzzled.

What were they doing? "I"ll swim over and see," thought Allin.

"Don't move, you silly young thing," barked a voice close by.

"Gracious me," answered Allin, "I thought you were a large log."

"Sh," said the old alligator. "Be quiet."

Allin was so curious about this great huge alligator that he could scarcely control himself. Finally the men in the boat moved farther downstream and Allin swam over to the old alligator. Allin was very curious, but also cautious. He didn't get too close.

"What were the men doing, sir?" asked Allin respectfully.

"Hunting of course," snapped the old 'gator.

"Are we good to eat?" asked Allin.

"They only want our hides," replied the old 'gator. "Men make fine shoes, purses and other things from alligator skins. No man is your friend. Remember that, young alligator. If you want to grow old and large like me, stay hidden when men or boats are around."

"Will I ever be as big as you?" gasped Allin in delight. "How old are you?"

The old 'gator glared at the little alligator. "That is not a polite question, young fellow. But I will answer you anyway. I am ten years old and I am almost ten feet long. I weigh about three hundred pounds. If you are careful and eat lots of fish, turtles, ducks, crabs and shrimp, you will grow too."

"I'm one year old today," said Allin proudly, still keeping a safe distance from the old 'gator. "Now I have learned to protect and care for myself. I hunt for my own food, instead of waiting for my mother to bring it. Today I'm going to find a cave in the bank of the swamp for my home. When the weather is cold, I will stay in my den and sleep. When the sun is hot, I'll swim and maybe rest on the shore close to the water."

The old 'gator snorted, "That sounds like a good plan. Why don't you stop bothering me and get busy?"

Allin decided that it was time to go. Off he swam in search of a home.

He would remember the advice of the wise old alligator. He would be on the watch for men hunting for his skin. Allin was determined to grow to be a wise old alligator too.

Jean Ellis

Water Is a Lovely Thing

Water is a lovely thing—
Dark and ripply in a spring,
Dark and quiet in a pool,
In a puddle, brown and cool;
In the river, blue and grey,
In a fountain, crystal bright;
In a pitcher, frosty cold,
In a bubble, pink and gold;
In a happy summer sea,
Just as green as green can be;
In a rainbow far unfurled,
Every colour in the world;
All the year from spring to spring,
Water is a lovely thing.

Julia W. Wolfe

Water All Around Us

Can you guess the name of the most precious material on earth? It is not gold, or diamonds, or oil. It is not rare at all, and you do not have to buy it. It has no colour. Nothing could live without it. You drink it. Have you guessed what it is? It is WATER.

There is much more water on earth than there is land. Most of the water is in the oceans.

Try to imagine how big the oceans are. They are thousands of miles wide. They are very, very deep in some places. If you could put the highest mountain into the deepest part of the ocean, the mountain would be covered with water.

Look around you right now. Perhaps you do not see any water at all. But it is there, just the same.

More than half of your own body is made of water. Growing plants have water in them, too. Even things that look as hard and dry as wood have a little water in them.

Many other things look quite solid, too, but they are really full of holes. The holes are too tiny to see, and that is where the water hides. It is like the water inside a wet sponge. You cannot see the water until you squeeze it out.

You would be surprised to know how much water there is in your food. There are three glasses of water in every quart of ice cream. Half of a hamburger is water.

A watermelon would be only as big as a baseball if you took away all the water. A loaf of bread looks quite dry, but it has a whole glass of water in it.

So you always get some water in the food that you eat. It seems like a lot, but it is not enough for good health. You must also drink several glasses of water every day.

When is water as hard as stone? When it freezes and becomes ICE.

Ice is very strong. It holds you up when you skate across a frozen pond. Eskimos in the far north sometimes build their houses out of blocks of ice.

Water becomes bigger when it turns into ice. It spreads out and takes up more room. If you put a bottle full of water outdoors on a very cold day, the water will freeze. You will see the ice sticking up out of the bottle. You may cover the bottle as tightly as you can, but you will not stop the push of the ice. It will crack the glass.

Nothing can keep water from pushing out as it freezes. Even a strong iron water pipe will be broken if water freezes in it.

Sometimes there is water in cracks in the street. If the water freezes, the ice will break up the pavement.

Ice can break up huge rocks, too. Sometimes there is rain water in the holes and cracks of a rock. If the weather gets very cold, the water freezes. It must get bigger and push out. The pushing makes the rock crack and break into pieces.

Have you ever seen heaps of stones lying at the bottom of a cliff? They were once part of the big rocks above. The pieces fell when ice broke them off.

And did you know that many mountains and valleys were carved by giant pieces of ice which moved slowly down from the north thousands of years ago?

Ice, you see, has been here for a long time.

When does ice disappear? When it melts and becomes water again. And imagine what the world would be like without water. There would be no food; in fact, there would be no plant or animal life at all! And that is why water is more precious than gold, diamonds or oil. We could live without these things, but nothing could live without water.

Mae and Ira Freeman

Sea Shells
on the Shore

All afternoon we paddled on
     in search of oyster shells . . .
We saw shells shaped like fishes and
     we saw shells shaped like bells,
We found a thousand mussel shells
     and cockles by the score,
And shabby little barnacles
     all washed up on the shore.

There were shells as sharp as razors,
     and strange shells shaped like shoes,
There were shells like pudding dishes,
     and trumpet shells to choose;
But all we wanted, really, was
     and oyster shell or two,
So we could find a shiny pearl
     all shimmering and new.

Will Stratford

The Great Water Beetle

During the summer the boys paid many visits to the pond. Each time they went there they saw something to interest them.

Their uncle taught them to keep perfectly still while looking into the water. They soon came to know that this was the best way to study pond-life, for, whenever they moved, the creatures they were watching would dart out of sight.

One day, while they were both lying on the bank gazing into the pond, a huge black beetle came up to the surface of the water. It remained there for a few moments, with its head hanging downward and its tail sticking right out of the water. Then it dived down out of sight. In a few minutes it came up again, and this time Frank's net was under it before it could escape.

Just as Frank was putting it into the glass jar, Tom whispered, "Here is another one—quick, Frank!"

But Frank was too late; for before he could get the first beetle into the jar the second one had dived to the bottom of the pond. The boys waited for a long time, hoping to see the other beetle again. At last their patience was rewarded. The beetle came up again to the surface. As soon as it did so, in went the net, and out came beetle number two.

"What big beauties," said Frank. "I wonder what they are. Let us hurry home and show them to Uncle George."

When they got home, their uncle placed the two beetles in a glass tank by themselves, so that they could be more easily observed.

"What do you call them, uncle?" asked Frank. "We have never seen such large, handsome beetles before."

"Have you not?" his uncle replied. "I am surprised at that, for this beetle is found in nearly all our ponds and ditches. It has a long Latin name, which means 'bordered diver,' but it is commonly known as the diving beetle. There are several kinds of these diving beetles. This is the largest. Can you give me an idea of their size?"

And Uncle George handed Frank a small measuring-rule which he carried in his pocket.

Frank looked at the beetles, and then moved his thumb-nail along the rule.

"About an inch and a half in length," he said.

"That is about right," said his uncle. "Are these two beetles exactly alike?"

"They are both about the same shape and colour. One is slightly bigger than the other. They are both greenish-black above and brown below. There is a curious broad border of yellow all round the edge of their bodies," said Tom.

"But they are not both exactly alike," said Frank. "I notice that one is smooth on the back, while the other's back is all grooved."

"You are right, Frank," said Uncle George. "The one with the grooved wing-cases is the female. The one with the smooth cases is the male.

"Notice the long legs they have for swimming, and how they seem to oar themselves through the water. Notice also that the male has a large flat disk upon each of his forelegs. These are suckers, by which he can cling to things."

"Why do they come up to the surface so often?" Frank asked.

"They cannot live without air. They carry a supply of air under their wing-cases. They just come up to renew it from time to time. This is done by thrusting the end of their bodies out of the water, as you can easily see."

"One would think they ought to thrust their heads out to get air," said Tom.

"That seems most natural to us, because we breathe with our mouths," said Uncle George. "These animals take in air with their tails. A great many pond-insects breathe in this curious way."

"What do they eat?" Frank asked.

"They are fierce, greedy creatures," his uncle replied. "They attack and kill worms, tadpoles, and even small fishes."

Uncle George threw a small worm into the tank. One of the beetles seized it at once and began to devour it greedily. Presently the other beetle seized an end of the worm. The boys watched closely, and saw that the beetles' jaws moved from side to side like a pair of pincers.

Next morning, when Uncle George and the boys went in to see the beetles, they found only one in the tank. The other had escaped during the night. After a careful search they found it, at the far end of the room, dead.

"Now, how do you think this beetle managed to get out of the tank and travel all that way?" Uncle George asked.

"It must have crawled up the inside of the tank, then down the outside. Then it must have fallen off the window-sill, and crawled right across the floor," said Frank.

Uncle George shook his head.

"It might," he said, "have managed to crawl up to the edge of the tank so long as its legs were wet. But as its long legs are made for swimming, and not for crawling with, I can hardly see how it could have crawled or walked all that distance."

"Then how did it get there, Uncle George?"

In answer to Frank's question, his uncle took the dead beetle, and placed it on a piece of paper on the table. He next moved aside each of the large black wing-cases with a pin.

Underneath these wing-cases the boys saw a pair of large wings neatly folded up. Uncle George removed one of the wing-cases and unfolded one of the wings. Stretched out, it was longer than the beetle's body, and it seemed to be made up of thin, clear skin, stretched on a framework of long, thin supports.

"Why, these beetles can fly," said Tom.

"Of course they can," said his uncle. "All beetles can fly. This creature has evidently been flying about the room all night. These insects are furnished with wings, so that they may be able to fly to another pool when food gets scarce, or when their pool dries up.

W. S. Cameron

The Right Time To Laugh

In a dense Australian thicket, a lyrebird scratching in the ground once found a choice bit of food. So he spread his tail and rejoiced.

Just then along came a frog. "Good morning, friend," said the frog, and he sat very solemnly by, waiting to be invited to eat a share of the feast. But the lyrebird took his food and flew up into a tree.

"My friend," said the frog, feeling injured, "yesterday you dined with me, haven't you one morsel to spare for me today?"

"Certainly!" said the lyrebird, for he did not wish to appear so greedy as he was! "You may have a bite of my food. Just come right up and get it!"

"I can't come up," said the frog. "I've no wings with which to fly, and my feet were not made for climbing."

But the lyrebird, looking about, spied a vine trailing down from the tree with one end on the ground.

"Take hold of the vine," said he, "and I will pull you up." So the frog caught hold of the vine and the lyrebird pulled him up slowly until he was on a level with the branch where the lyrebird was sitting.

"I thank you, my friend," said the frog, and he was about to hop down beside the food he desired, when the lyrebird let go of the vine and dropped the frog—plump! —to the ground. Then the lyrebird, thinking he had played a very fine joke on his friend, laughed and laughed and he ate his dinner up all by himself.

But the frog was very angry. He sat down below and sulked, thinking of nothing but the trick which the lyrebird had played on him.

"Well, I'll pay him back!" the frog told himself. "I'll pay him back, I will!"

So he hopped to the neighbouring river, where the lyrebird got his water, and he drank and drank and drank. He drank till he swallowed not only all the water in that river, but all the water in all the rivers and all the lakes in Australia! Then he sat, quite puffed out with the water he had swallowed, and solemnly blinked his eyes.

Soon the lyrebird wanted a drink; but where was he to get it? There wasn't a river to turn to! The lyrebird got thirstier and thirstier until he was half-crazy for want of a drink of water. At last he was sufficiently punished for the wicked prank he had played to be very sorry for what he had done. And alas! he wasn't the only one who suffered; for not a beast or a bird in all Australia could get a drink of water. One by one, they went to the frog and begged him to give out the waters. Dingo, the wild dog, went; Spiny, the anteater, went; Flying-fox, the great bat, went. And they said:

"Great frog, the lyrebird has done you wrong, but now he is very sorry and you are making us suffer who did you no wrong at all. Give forth the waters, we pray you."

But still the great frog sulked and would not answer a word. Then the lyrebird himself went before him and humbly begged his pardon. But the frog held, stubborn as ever, to the memory of his wrongs and he would not forgive the lyrebird. He sat as puffed up as before and solemnly blinked his eyes.

Then the great black swan went before him, and the white eagle, and the emu, and all the other birds and beasts. But no matter how they besought him, he would not give back the water. So at length the birds and the beasts all got together and said:

"If the old frog only knew how ridiculous he is sulking away like that, he would laugh at himself; then the

waters would gush from his mouth."

"Ah!" cried the anteater. "If that is the case, let us make him laugh and give up the rivers."

So they all stood in a circle about the solemn old frog and performed their funniest antics. First, they brought out the duck-billed mole, and a funny enough fellow he was! They backed him up to the frog and from the mole's furry back, Mr. Frog expected, of course, to see the face of a beast. Then they turned the mole around quickly. Lo, there was the face of a bird with a flat, absurd bill like a duck's in the place where his snout ought to be! But the frog never smiled the least smile.

At last they brought out an eel, and that was a happy thought. The eel stood up on the tip of his long, long tail and he danced. He wiggled and wriggled and twisted. At that, the corners of the frog's mouth began all at once to turn up, his lips began to twitch: his nose began to wrinkle, and all of a sudden—Hah! He opened his mouth big and wide and he let out a mighty laugh. He laughed and he laughed and he laughed; and, as he laughed, the waters gushed forth from his mouth and filled up all the rivers and all the lakes in Australia.

"I was a silly old frog to sulk like that!" he cried.

Then the lyrebird, and the wild dog, and the anteater, and the flying-fox, and the opossum, and the black swan, and the white eagle, and the emu, and duck-billed mole, and the kangaroo all hurried to get the drink which they so sorely needed.

Florence Beaupré Miller

If I Had a Horse

If I had a horse,
I'd like him to be
As white as the whitecaps
That ride on the sea.

Or I'd like him black
And little and trim;
Or if he were chestnut
I'd be proud of him;

(Franz Marc, "Blue Horses", 1911.
Collection: Walker Art Center, Minneapolis, Minnesota.)

I'd like him large,
A smooth dappled grey,
With heavy hoofs;
Or I'd like him bay.

You see it's like this:
I just wouldn't mind
What was his size
Or his colour or kind;

If I had a horse
I'd like him so much
I just wouldn't care
About colours and such.

Lucretia Penny

193

Whitey and the Rustlers

It was a fine spring morning in Lone Tree County, with the prairie beginning to turn green, and the wild chokecherry and plum thickets smelling sweet. Magpies and meadow larks were talking big about the business of starting new nests.

Whitey was headed for Cedar Spring to see if the windmill was working, but along the way he was looking for his two beef steers, which he ran with Uncle Torwal's cattle. He hadn't noticed them around for several days, and was a little worried.

Old Spot jogged along at his special ambling trot and thought about the days when he'd been a first-class cow horse. Whitey sat up straight and thought about the fine new saddle he'd buy in the fall when he sold those two steers of his.

He didn't really mind wearing a hand-me-down Stetson of Uncle Torwal's, especially when it had such a fine rattlesnake hatband, for most all cowboys wore battered old hats. And for the same reason he didn't mind the old boots with the run-over heels and the fancy butterfly stitching on the tops, that he'd been given by a puncher with small feet.

But his old saddle was something else again. It was so old the corners of the skirts were curled up tight, and the strings had long ago been chewed off by calves. Everywhere the stitching was coming undone, leaving great corners of old leather sticking up to give the whole affair the look of a moulting hen. Furthermore, the stirrups were the clumsy iron kind. For a long time, Whitey had felt that the saddle spoiled his whole appearance, making him look more like a homesteader than a cowboy.

Of course, when he'd been smaller and first come to live with Uncle Torwal and help him run the Lone Tree Ranch, it hadn't mattered so much. But now that he was getting on to ten years old and practically a top hand he had to think more about the appearance of his equipment. People set a lot of store by such things.

So last summer Uncle Torwal had given him two Whiteface calves. Together they figured out a brand for him, and sent it off to be registered after they'd put it on the calves. It was a fine big squiggle on the ribs with three dots at the end.

The Rattlesnake brand, they called it. Whitey figured it was about as fine a brand as he knew of. He saw no reason why it shouldn't someday be as famous as the old "101". And Rattlesnake Ranch sounded good no matter how you said it!

So he rode on for a while, thinking about the time when the rattlesnake brand would be on thousands of head of good beef cattle instead of only two, and he'd be able to have a new saddle every week if he felt like it. But just when he had started thinking about how fine a Sunday saddle would look, decorated with silver in the Western fashion, he came on a calf bogged in the mud around an old water hole, so he had to stop thinking about saddles for a while.

The old cow nearby was in a nasty humour, bawling and swinging her tail, so he didn't feel it was safe to get down off Spot. That meant he'd have to rope the calf and drag it out. And as calves will do, that one had gotten out into the middle of the softest patch of gumbo, so that if Whitey missed his first cast, as he most usually did, he was bound to get his rope all muddy. That never did any throw rope any good, and was especially bad for a brand-new one like Whitey was carrying. He finally urged old Spot out onto the mud until he could reach down and drop the loop square on the calf.

After that he took a hitch around the saddle horn and in no time at all dragged the calf out onto solid ground. After he'd shaken the loop loose and the cow and calf had gone he found his rope was muddy after all, so he had to get off and find some dry grass to clean it with.

It was then he noticed the fuss a bunch of magpies were making in a little gully not far off, and decided to go see what it was they were doing. The rain the day before had washed deeply into a pile of dirt that had caved off the cutbank, exposing some corners of what looked to be cowhides, fresh enough to attract the magpies.

After some tugging and digging, Whitey uncovered three hides, which had apparently been carelessly buried by caving part of the bank onto them. Two hides carried his Rattlesnake brand, and the other Uncle Torwal's Lone Tree!

He sat down on the bank, and if he hadn't been almost a man grown he'd have bawled like a kid, for there went his hopes of a new saddle. The two Rattlesnake steers he'd counted on so much were now in some rustler's truck on the road to a butcher shop far off. He knew how the rustlers operated, going out at night with a truck and butchering two or three steers quickly, destroying the hides to prevent identification, and leaving to sell the meat before anyone knew they were about.

There'd been talk for some time that they must be operating around here, for ranchers all up and down the valley had been missing beef, but until now there hadn't been any kind of proof.

When Whitey rode into the ranch and up to the horse trough, Torwal saw he looked mighty glum, but didn't say anything.

"Truck rustlers been getting our cattle," Whitey said as Spot was drinking.

"There's been talk of such," Torwal said. "But nobody knows for sure that I know of."

"I found three fresh hides over by Cedar Spring this morning," Whitey said. "They were buried in a washout." He brushed dust off his hat and waited for Uncle Torwal to ask him some more. He was trying his best to talk as any cowboy would, instead of getting excited like a kid.

Torwal saw there must be more to the story, because three beef steers missing shouldn't make Whitey look so upset. So he said, casual like, "Were the brands cut out?" For usually the rustlers cut the brand out and burn it before burying the hide.

"Reckon they must have been careless this time," Whitey said. "One was a Lone Tree steer and the other two were Rattlesnake brand."

"Got both yours, did they?" Torwal said, and whistled. "That was tough goin', cleanin' out your whole spread."

"That's a fact," Whitey said. "Looks like I'll ride this old hull a while longer." And he led Spot into the stable so Uncle Torwal wouldn't see how badly he really did feel.

They didn't say much as they cooked and ate dinner, but afterwards, as they sat on the porch, Torwal spoke up. "Reckon we might as well ride in and see the police," he said. "Now that we know for sure that rustlers are working around here, maybe we can figure out something."

"I sure hope so," Whitey said. "They did me out of a new saddle and I wish I was old enough to swear!"

When they got to town they tied their horses and walked into the police office. Sergeant Smith shook hands

with them while Constable Wilkerson dragged out chairs.

After some polite talk of this and that, Torwal told the sergeant what Whitey had found.

"Were those hides fresh, son?" Sergeant Smith asked Whitey.

"Yessir, they looked to be only a day or two there," Whitey told him.

"This is the first time we've had any proof," the sergeant said, "but there have been a lot of complaints of missin' beef critturs all up and down the valley."

"How do you reckon they get in and out of the valley without anyone knowing?" Torwal wondered after a little.

"I've been considering that myself," Sergeant Smith told him. "They have to come through here or through Hill City to get in or out, and we've been watchin' both places close, yet nobody has seen any strangers or strange trucks."

"I wish we could catch them," Whitey spoke up. "I was going to get a new saddle with the money from my steers!"

"Well, maybe you can figure how to catch them and use your share of the reward money for that saddle," Constable Wilkerson told him.

At the mention of REWARD, Whitey stopped looking at the posters and notices tacked over the sergeant's desk and brightened right up. "You mean there's a reward for those rustlers?" he asked.

"Sure," the sergeant told him. "I got the notice around here somewhere."

After some more talk they shook hands with the sergeant and the constable and rode off towards the ranch.

As they rode along Whitey thought about that reward, and tried to figure out some way he could earn it. It seemed to him that getting a new saddle by trapping rustlers was even better than getting it by selling cattle.

"Uncle Torwal!" he said, suddenly remembering something. "A time or two lately I've noticed tracks of a truck or car up in that limestone canyon the other side of Cedar Spring. I just figured it was somebody building fence, but it might be where those rustlers are getting into the canyon, do you suppose?"

Torwal thought a while. "It could be, maybe," he said. "There used to be an old road through there that went down into the Boxelder Road. Maybe we might as well drop by and take a look at things up there."

They found that the old trail, which had for years been overgrown and washed out in places, did show signs of use. The worst holes had been filled, and while it was still not a road one would drive for pleasure, it was plain that a truck could travel over it.

"Looks like this might be it, all right," Torwal allowed. "This trail comes out on the Boxelder Road, where nobody would think of watching for them."

"Why don't we lay for them when they come back?" Whitey asked, thinking of the reward and his new saddle.

"Well," said Torwal, "they might not come back. Those dudes are pretty smart and don't often work the same place twice. That's why they are so hard to catch." After seeing how Whitey's face fell, he went on, "On the other hand, with a trick road like this they might feel safe for a while longer. From all the talk of missing cattle in the valley, they must have made several trips already."

"Tell you what," Torwal said after they'd started home. "We might take turns watching that canyon evenings for a while, just in case they did come back."

"Yessir!" Whitey agreed. "We'll catch 'em coming in and collect the rewards!"

"We don't want to bother them comin' in," Torwal corrected him. "We just want to know when they come in so we'll have time to call the police and catch them going out with the meat in the trucks for evidence."

Whitey still favoured capturing the rustlers without interference from the police, but he said nothing about it. He was bound he'd get that saddle the rustlers had done him out of and even part of the reward would be enough.

"I'll take my blankets and go out right away to watch for them," he said.

"You won't need any blankets," Torwal told him. "Those fellers usually figure to come in just about

sundown so they'll be able to locate the critturs they want before the dusk is gone. So if they aren't in sight by full dark they'll probably not come."

After Whitey had eaten an early supper and was leaving to watch the canyon, Uncle Torwal spoke up. "If they don't show up tonight, we'll take turns with the neighbours for a few nights."

"I don't want anyone to take turns," Whitey hollered. "I'm the one they cleaned out, and I'll watch every night!"

So every night for almost a week Whitey rode out to a small butte where he could watch the canyon. Every night he carefully hid Spot in a plum thicket and then crawled Indian fashion to the top of the butte, where he lay hidden in the bushes like some oldtime scout. But nothing happened, and he was beginning to believe the rustlers had deserted the valley.

On the seventh night, he'd just started down to go home when he thought he heard a truck motor. He hurried back up the hill and the sound was plain there. It was a powerful motor, and working hard. Soon he could see the dimmed lights as they moved cautiously to the mouth of the canyon, where they were switched off and the motor stopped.

It was rustlers, sure enough!

Whitey had been complaining to himself because Uncle Torwal wouldn't let him bring his rifle and capture the rustlers single-handed, but tonight he thought of nothing but getting back to the ranch as soon as possible to tell Uncle Torwal and get word to Sergeant Smith. It seemed to him then that it was really police business to deal with such people.

Spot got the surprise of his life when Whitey clapped spurs and quirt onto him! He couldn't remember the last time he'd travelled faster than a trot. But as this seemed to be in the nature of a special occasion he did his best, and before long Whitey and Torwal were sitting out by the road waiting for the police to come by and pick them up. The word had spread, and by the time the sergeant got there, ranchers and cowboys from up and down the valley had gathered. Most of them carried rifles on their saddles, or pistols in their belts. Rustlers were not popular thereabouts, and Whitey was looking forward to a right exciting time when they caught up with them.

When the sergeant came they all went along to Cedar Spring and the little canyon. Whitey had been afraid someone would think to tell him to stay behind, but no one did, so he rode along.

The men had all been concealed in the plum thickets for what seemed a mighty long time to Whitey, when they heard the truck coming back.

"This is when the bullets start to fly!" Whitey thought, as Sergeant Smith stepped out into the light of the truck and held up his hand. But the truck stopped without protest. Police and ranch men flashed on flashlights and swarmed all around it. Four weaselly-looking men climbed carefully out and stood with their hands raised while they and the truck were searched.

"There's plenty of beef in here!" a constable hollered.

"All right!" the sergeant answered. "One of you drive the truck along behind me, and we'll haul these fellows down to our jail for a spell."

The rustlers didn't say anything, except to sort of mutter to themselves. They didn't look like the tough guys Whitey had been picturing in his mind. They weren't wearing gun belts, and they didn't talk tough to the sergeant. Worst of all, they wore bib overalls, like farmers, and one even had on a straw hat and plow shoes! Whitey was mighty disappointed in them.

Early next morning Whitey and Uncle Torwal went to town, and Mr. Beasly, editor of the *Lone Tree Eagle,* interviewed Whitey.

The reward turned out to be only fifty dollars, and that divided six ways, so there was not enough to buy the saddle with. Whitey had built his hopes so high on that reward, that he felt mighty bad for a few days. But after reading what Mr. Beasly wrote about him in the paper, how his alertness had helped make Lone Tree County free of rustlers and the like, he sort of got used to the idea of getting along with the old saddle another year.

Then one morning Torwal told him, "We have to go to town this morning, Bub. Sergeant Smith said something about wanting to see you."

All the way into town Whitey wondered what the sergeant could want. He imagined this and that, but never thought of the real answer. For after some talk the sergeant pointed to something tied up in a grain sack on the floor and told Whitey, "Some fellow left that here and told me to give it to you."

Whitey opened it up and inside was a brand-new saddle, the decorations hand-tooled, and the whang-leather tie strings shining bright yellow, the sheepskin lining bright and clean, and the whole thing smelling of neat's foot oil and new leather. It was the most beautiful saddle Whitey had ever seen. On the back of the cantle was a small silver plate he'd missed at first. It was engraved:

TO WHITEY
FOR SERVICE IN RIDDING
LONE TREE COUNTY OF RUSTLERS
FROM THE LONE TREE STOCKMAN'S
ASS'N.

Whitey couldn't think of anything to say, so he just grinned and carried the saddle out to try how it looked on Spot.

Glen Rounds

A Horse Afraid of His Shadow

One day, long, long ago, in the land of Macedonia, the horse market was crowded with buyers. King Philip II, himself, was there. With him were the keepers of his royal stables. A fine lot of horses had been gathered for selling. First choice would go the King and his warriors.

With King Philip stood his young son, Alexander, who was twelve years old. None in that throng of buyers had a better eye for a good horse than this lad. No boys of his own age could compare with the young Alexander in horsemanship.

"Look well at all the animals, my son," King Philip said. "Then tell me which ones you would choose from among them."

"Many of these colts are well formed, my father." The boy spoke with sure tones. "Many have spirit. They would ride bravely to battle. But none is so noble as that young black stallion yonder, that one with the white mark shaped like an ox's head on his face."

"The young Prince chooses well," the black stallion's owner cried. "That is indeed the finest colt in all the market today. My price for him is high; thirteen talents, in fact. But I will be honest with you, Your Majesty. That young black stallion will wear a saddle and bridle, but he will not be ridden. He is as wild as the North Wind. None can stay long upon his back." The black colt even then was prancing and snorting as the noisy crowd gathered round him.

"No other horse here can compare with that one," the boy, Alexander, insisted. "Surely skilled horsemen from the palace stables can tame him."

"Let the black stallion be ridden!" ordered King Philip.

The most daring horsemen of his court mounted the colt. But the trader had spoken truly. One after another, they were thrown from his back.

The colt started at every sound. As soon as someone tried to ride him away, he whirled and reared high. He gave one mighty twist, and the rider was gone from his back.

"Are you satisfied now, my son, that this horse is not worth buying?" the King asked Alexander.

"No, Father, I still say the black stallion is the very best in this market place. His riders do not understand him. Let me try my hand on his bridle."

The King was pleased with his son's courage. He had no fear for his safety. The boy knew how to fall off a horse quite as well as how to ride one.

"Ride him, then, Alexander!" the King said. "And if you can succeed where these others have failed, I will buy the horse for you."

The men in the horse market marvelled to see the fearless lad leap into the saddle. The trembling black horse stood still. The boy stroked his glossy neck, which shone like ebony. Alexander talked to the horse softly. Then he turned his head straight toward the afternoon sun and galloped away.

It grew late. The sun was dropping below the horizon when the anxious crowd in that market place saw the boy coming back. Like lightning, the black stallion was galloping, galloping, but the boy was still on his back. Easily Alexander pulled the spirited steed to a halt. He patted the sides of the stallion, which now seemed tame as a kitten.

"Well ridden, my son! The black stallion is yours," King Philip cried.

"Tell us your secret, young Prince," the palace horsemen asked. "How did you tame that wild spitfire so easily?"

"It was as I said," Alexander replied. "You did not understand him. This stallion is a horse of high and noble spirit. He starts at the sight of each moving thing that is strange to him. While the others were trying to ride him, I saw that what frightened him the most was his own moving shadow. When he ran from the sun, the black shadow leaped along, just under his nose. I took care to turn his face toward the sun, so that his shadow could not be seen. The horse forgot his fear. I let him gallop to his heart's content, and now he trusts me as his master."

The King wept for pride and joy in his son's wisdom and bravery. "One day you will make a great king, Alexander," he said to the Prince.

Anonymous

The Silly Slave

Once in Ephesus, an ancient city, there was a rich merchant who had a hard time finding a teacher for his children. When he found a man wise enough to teach the things he wanted his boys to learn, the man was so dull that he put the children to sleep in the classroom.

On the other hand, the teachers he found who were lively and told interesting stories were not wise enough to teach the lessons this man insisted on his children learning.

So it was that he went to the great slave market.

"Slavemaster," he said to the man who sold slaves, "I badly need a wise, but interesting, teacher for my young sons. I will pay many gold pieces for such a man. Also, if he can teach as I want my children taught, I will be so grateful that at the end of one year I will set the slave free."

Now when they heard this, all the slaves wanted very much to be the one chosen. They all started to shout and tell him how very wise they were.

That is, all shouted except one. He was a little man, scarcely larger than a child, but his face was so ugly it was funny. He looked so silly that the others called him the Little Clown Slave.

They were wrong in thinking him foolish. He was one of the wisest men who ever lived.

He did not, of course, know how really wise he was, but he knew that he was much smarter than the other slaves in the market. He also knew that his silly face would cause the rich merchant to pass him by unless he could do something to convince the merchant that he really was a wise teacher.

So while the others shouted to tell how wise they were, the little slave sat back planning how he could show the merchant that he was wiser than they.

"I think," he told himself, "that I had best tell him some of my little stories. Then he can see how I would teach his sons by telling them stories which they could love but which would also teach them a lesson."

Carefully he picked out a few of his stories that had good lessons to teach. The first proved that it is unwise to tell a lie just to be funny.

It was about a boy who loved to play tricks. He was a shepherd lad who tended flocks on the hills above Old Athens. One day he thought it would be a funny trick to frighten the other shepherds. So he ran down the hill shouting: "Wolf! Wolf! A wolf is eating the sheep!"

The other shepherds came running to kill the wolf and the trickster laughed very hard. He thought this very funny. But the very next day a real wolf attacked the flocks. Again the boy ran down the hill shouting: "Help! Help! Wolf! Wolf! A wolf is eating my sheep!"

This time no one came to help for they thought he was trying to trick them again. He lost all his sheep because he told a lie just to be funny.

The little slave also picked out two other stories to tell as well. These gave lessons in generosity and thrift.

While he was planning these stories, the merchant was testing the wisdom of different men. Finally he came to the little slave.

"O great master!" the little slave cried. "Let me tell you a wonderful t-t-t-t-"

He was so excited at the thought of earning his freedom that the words stuck in his throat.

He stopped and tried to start again.

"L---l-l-let me t-t-t-t-t------"

He just couldn't stop his stuttering. A tear squeezed out of his eye and plopped off the end of his ridiculous nose.

He looked so funny in his misery that the others started to laugh loudly.

The little slave took a deep breath and started again. This time he forced himself to speak slowly. His words were wise and beautiful.

But the merchant passed on. The noise of the laughter was so great that he did not hear a single word of the tale about the boy who cried wolf.

The merchant did not find the kind of teacher he wanted. So each time that new slaves were brought to Ephesus he came down to search again. The little slave always tried to attract his attention, but the merchant, remembering the other time, would not listen to him.

One day the rich merchant came to rent some slaves to carry goods to the king in the city of Sardis. The little slave was one of these.

The merchandise had been piled beside a warehouse where the slaves were sent to get it. The merchant came out to give orders to the slavemaster. As they passed the little slave, he looked slyly at his companions and then shouted loud enough for the merchant to hear.

"Quickly!" he cried. "Some of the bundles are small and some are large. The last ones to pick them up will have to carry the big ones! Quickly! Let's get the small ones!"

It was a long way to Sardis and all were eager to get the lighter loads. They all rushed forward. The little slave was the fastest one of them all. He was the first to reach the bundles.

But instead of grabbing the smallest, he chose the largest of them all—a woven reed basket covered with cloth.

"I win! I win!" he cried triumphantly.

The others laughed at his silliness. The merchant shook his head.

"I am not sure," he said to the slavemaster, "that I want anyone that silly carrying my goods. He might harm them."

"I will watch him very closely, master," said the overseer.

"But I am not silly at all!" the little slave cried. "I was smarter than all the others!"

"Oh?" said the merchant. "How do you think that? You had your choice of all the bundles, but you passed up the small ones and took instead the biggest of the lot."

"That was because I am wiser than they," the slave said stubbornly.

The merchant looked at the slavemaster. "He is crazy."

"Oh, no," the little slave said. "When I saw the bundles were of a different size, I asked myself why it should be so. Then I decided that the packers had made some small because their contents were very heavy—maybe of iron— so that a man could not carry a larger load.

"Then I asked myself why one basket should be so large and I told myself that it was because what was inside was lighter than the smaller bundles.

"Then I saw the breeze gently lift up one corner of the cloth covering the basket and discovered that it had bread inside.

"Now I knew that although some bundles were large and some were small, they were about the same weight, for the packers would try to make everyone's load equal.

"But I also knew that we slaves would be fed at noon and that this bread would be our meal. So by taking the largest of them all, I knew I would get no heavier a load than the others, but at noon my load would be all gone and I would have nothing to carry all afternoon! The rest would still have their heavy loads all the way to Sardis!"

The merchant smiled. "You are quite a trickster," he said. "Since you will have nothing to carry, I suppose you will help one of your friends."

"Oh, no," the slave replied. "I shall help them all. You see, O great master, I tell very fine stories. And as I walk along this afternoon, I shall tell them to my companions and it will take their minds off their burdens. That way I will help them all."

"Well!" said the merchant. "You are wiser than I thought."

"That is true, O great master," the little slave said. "I know that I look like a silly fool, but I am wise and I love to teach my fellow man. Since I look like a clown, none will listen to me when I say wise things. So I have hidden them in my stories. They think I only speak to amuse them, but my stories teach lessons as well. Would you like to hear one?"

"That I would," the merchant said thoughtfully, "but there is not time now. We must start for Sardis if we are to deliver the goods on time. So I tell you what we will do. I will have another slave hired to carry the bread. You will walk beside me and tell me one of those wise stories of yours."

This the little slave did and the merchant was so impressed with his wisdom that he bought him from the slave dealer. Unfortunately for the merchant he never got to use the slave for a teacher of his sons. He bragged about the little slave's wisdom to the king and the king insisted on having the wise little slave for his own. The merchant could not refuse to sell him to the king.

The king was so delighted with the slave's stories that he made him a free man.

This is not all the story for the little trickster's tales still teach us today. He was Aesop who wrote the Fables.

I. G. Edmonds

The Plaint of the Camel

Canary birds feed on sugar and seed,
    Parrots have crackers to crunch;
And as for the poodles, they tell me the noodles
    Have chickens and cream for their lunch.
      But there's never a question
      About *my* digestion—
      Anything does for me!

Cats, you're aware, can repose in a chair,
Chickens can roost upon rails;
Puppies are able to sleep in a stable,
And oysters can slumber in pails.
But no one supposes
A poor camel dozes—
Any place does for me!

Lambs are enclosed where it's never exposed,
Coops are constructed for hens;
Kittens are treated to houses well heated,
And pigs are protected by pens.
But a camel comes handy
Wherever it's sandy—
Anywhere does for me!

People would laugh if you rode a giraffe,
Or mounted the back of an ox;
It's nobody's habit to ride on a rabbit,
Or try to bestraddle a fox.
But as for a camel, he's
Ridden by families—
Any load does for me!

A snake is as round as a hole in the ground,
And weasels are wavy and sleek;
And no alligator could ever be straighter
Than lizards that live in a creek.
But a camel's all lumpy
And bumpy and humpy—
Any shape does for me!

Charles Edward Carryl

Ali and the Camels

In the long-ago days, Tripoli was well known for many things. But no one thing and no one person was better known than the great and illustrious Caliph, Ahmed Ben Hamed of Tripoli. One day the great Caliph decided to send some of his most handsome camels to the Sultan of Egypt as a symbol of his friendship. He called his faithful servant Ramadan, to his throne room.

"I wish to send ten of my finest camels to the Sultan of Egypt," he told the servant. "Choose them well, for they must please the Sultan. Then prepare yourself for the journey and be ready to start when the sun appears again in the sky."

Ramadan was astonished by his master's command, for he knew little of desert life.

"I pray that you will let me find someone who knows more about desert life than I," Ramadan said humbly. "Let me find a desert Arab who knows the stars and who can follow the course of the sun. Such a person would not lose your camels as I might."

"Very well," the Caliph said. "Find such a man and send him on his way."

And so it was that Ramadan wandered through all the bazaars of the city, looking for a man of the desert. Finally, when his search seemed hopeless, he saw a man wearing the robes of a desert tribe.

"Are you from the desert, my friend?" Ramadan asked.

"Yes," the Arab replied. "My name is Ali. I came to the city to find work. My sheep have died. My crops have failed. If I do not find a job my family will starve."

"Then I have a job for you," the servant said. "My master needs someone to take ten camels to Cairo as a gift to the Sultan. He will pay you well—in gold. If you know your way through the desert and can follow the course of the sun and the stars, you can have the job."

"Oh, yes," Ali shouted for joy. "I have lived all my years in the desert and know it well."

The servant was pleased and he took Ali with him to the Caliph's palace. Once there he showed him the camel stables and said, "Here are ten camels. You are to take them to Cairo and give them to the Sultan."

Ali looked at the camels and then scratched the small white cap he wore on his head. "You say there are ten camels here," he said. "But let me count them to see if you are not trying to fool me."

Quickly Ali arranged the camels in a straight line. "Now I will count them," he said. "One-two-three-four-five-six-five-seven-six-eight. Eight! Ah-hah! There are only eight camels here. You rascal. You said there were ten. You have tried to trick me."

Realizing then that Ali could not count, Ramadan did not become upset. Instead he suggested another way of counting so that Ali could understand how many camels were before him.

"I have not tricked you," Ramadan said gently. "But because you have difficulty counting the camels, let us try another way. Try this. Pat each camel on the nose, and as you do so, bend a finger down like this. Then it will be easy for you to know how many camels you have."

To help Ali, Ramadan patted each camel on the nose, bent down each finger, and said, "See, I have patted the noses of all the camels and all my fingers are bent."

Then Ali tried to follow Ramadan's example, and when he had finished, he found that all of his fingers were bent, also.

"Now," said Ramadan hopefully. "Your fingers are all bent. How many camels are there?"

"Two handsful," Ali replied. But I don't know how many in numbers because I don't know how many fingers I have!"

Ramadan tried not to get angry, but he was losing his patience. "Open your fingers slowly," he said firmly. "And say a number as you open each one. Then you will know the number."

Slowly Ali opened his fingers. "Ten-nine-eight-seven-six-five-four-three-two-one-none. Well, I'll be! According to this way of counting, there are no camels at all. But I can see them right before me as plain as I see the moon at night."

Ramadan was almost ready to dismiss Ali and look for another Arab to take the camels to the Sultan of Egypt. But it was late and desert Arabs were scarce, and his master had ordered him to have the camels on their way by morning.

So he decided to try one more time. He took a piece of string and put ten beads on it. He knotted both ends well.

"Now," he said "Do not concern yourself with counting the camels. On this string I have placed beads, one for each animal. Now pat each camel on the nose and pass a bead from the top of the string to the bottom as you do so. When you have finished with the counting, all the beads will be at the bottom, and the count will be right."

"If you should have a bead left over, then you have lost a camel," Ramadan continued. "And if you have a camel left over, then Allah has given it to you and you may do with it what you wish."

Understanding this method, Ali took the string with the ten beads on it, and the ten camels, and enough food and water for many days, and began his long journey to Cairo.

After travelling through the desert sands for several hours Ali became very hot and tired. The sand was deep and burned his feet, and he could go only short distances before he was forced to stop and rest. Finally, as he stopped at an oasis to drink and count the camels, he had an idea.

"Why should I walk through this hot, deep sand?" he thought. "I have ten camels right here and I could be riding one. Camels do not mind walking in the sand. Their feet are made for it. As for me, my poor feet are getting burned with every step I take. I think I shall ride a camel."

So Ali mounted the first camel, and led the others after him. After some time he counted the camels again, letting one bead go from the top of the string to the bottom each time he patted the nose of a camel. He started counting, however, with the second camel, completely forgetting the one he was riding. Thus he discovered he had one bead left over.

When Ali saw the extra bead, he was frightened. "The rope must have been broken," he thought, "and a camel must have strayed. I must go back to the last place I counted to see if I can find it."

So Ali turned the camels around and headed back over the burning sand to the small oasis. But he found no camel.

"This can mean only one thing," Ali thought. "The great Allah has given me an extra bead."

So he took the bead off the string and to Ali the number of beads and the number of camels were again the same.

Ali turned his camels around and started again on his journey. He travelled until the sun was sinking in the west and the desert was getting cool. Soon he came to an oasis where a small spring of cold water flowed, and the palm trees swayed in the slight breeze. A few tents belonging to other travellers surrounded the area.

Ali got down from his camel, got out his piece of string, and began to count the animals. This time he had the camels in a half circle around him so he started with the one he had been riding. Thus he found that he had one camel for which there was no bead.

"Praise be to Allah!" Ali shouted. "He has seen fit to send me a camel for my food tonight, and I may share it with the others who are gathered here. Praise be to Allah!"

So Ali took out his long knife and killed the camel for which there was no bead. Then he called the other travellers and invited them to feast with him.

The next morning before Ali started on his journey, he counted the camels, and the number of beads and camels were just the same. Then he climbed up on the first camel and moved out into the desert.

After several hours had passed, he once again took out his string and checked the number of animals. Overlooking the camel he was riding, Ali found that there was one bead more than camels. So he threw the bead away.

That same evening when he made camp he stood on the sand and counted the camels just as he had done the night before. This time he found that there was one camel too many. "Given to me by Allah," he thought. So he killed the camel and called the other travellers to join him in feast.

And so it was on the next day, and on the next, and each day that followed. Ali found himself during the day with an extra bead, which he threw away, and at night with an extra camel, which he ate.

Finally, on the eleventh day of his journey, Ali walked into the city of Cairo holding only a piece of string in his dirty hand. Not understanding what he had done, he still proceeded to the Sultan's palace and asked to see the great ruler.

"This piece of string," Ali said, as he bowed before the Sultan, "is from the Caliph of Tripoli. He sends it with his greetings. He also said something about camels and beads, but it must have been very unimportant, for I have forgotten the message."

Naturally the Sultan was surprised by the Caliph's gift and able to make very little sense from Ali's words. Thinking that the heat of the desert must have affected the man's mind, the Sultan ordered food and drink.

Although Ali appreciated the Sultan's kindness, he was able to eat very little of the food. To be truthful, he was much too full of camel meat.

Robert Gilstrap and Irene Estabrook

231

Rumble Becomes a Tongue Twister

Rumble stared at the deep blue sky and the long fingers of white cloud above him, then he stared at the parched olive-brown acacia trees and the burnt-up elephant grass below. He'd done it again! He'd overwished, and here he was, a second time, making a spectacle of himself!

He glanced at a troop of baboons who were laughing themselves silly at him from down on the ground.

"Hello, Rumble!" they shouted. "What's the weather forecast up there? Cool and cloudy? Wet and windy? Can we expect a snowstorm when your tail carries you away?" And they rolled helplessly around, slapping each others' backs and screaming like mad things.

But by the time Rumble had thought up an answer that would squash even the rudest baboon, his tail had whisked him another three miles further on, and not even his enormous voice would carry that far.

Not that an answer mattered. Rumble was beginning to enjoy himself again, and the opinion of an animal that wasn't sure whether it wanted to look like an ape or a dog couldn't have troubled him less.

"Wheee!" he shouted, as his magnificient tail twirled and twisted him high above the trees. "Wheee!"

After a lifetime of plodding on the ground, envying the birds that soared above him, this whirling through the air was fun! Gaily, he plucked a small branch from a tree as he whizzed past and waved it vigorously round his head like a flag.

"Look out!" cried a muffled voice in his ear. "You'll have me seasick! What do you think you're doing?"

Rumble was so startled that he forgot to hold on to his wish and tumbled helter-skelter back down to earth again. It was fortunate that he wasn't very high up, and it was even more fortunate that his skin was so thick and tough, for with an earth-shattering crash he landed head-first into the prickliest thorn bush he'd ever been unlucky enough to meet. The most fortunate thing about the whole matter was that the branch he was carrying fell on top of him. If it had not, there would have been no voice left to scold him.

"You clumsy, great, lolloping creature!" it said. "Why can't you be more careful!"

Gingerly, Rumble wriggled himself backwards out of the thorn bush. He pulled half a dozen long grey spikes out of his nose. Then he picked up the branch and peered at it. A little green chameleon was still clinging to one of the twigs.

"You think you're mighty clever, don't you?" snapped the chameleon.

"Yes, I do," Rumble agreed. "After all, *you've* never seen a rhino flying before, have you?"

"No, I haven't! And I don't want to again. It's not natural."

"Of course it's not natural!" Rumble answered, huffily. "That's what makes it so clever."

"Does it, indeed?" said the chameleon. "Well, then, if I were to show you something *really* clever, would you admit that a flying rhinoceros is just about the silliest thing in creation?"

"Huh!" snapped Rumble. "*If* you were to show me . . . but I don't think you can."

"We'll see about that," answered the chameleon. "Now, then, I want you to stare at me. Stare straight at my eyes. Right at both of them, and watch carefully."

Rumble couldn't believe that the chameleon could really do anything clever. But he did as he was asked and stared at the lizard's hooded, bulging eyes. Slowly, as he watched, one of the eyes began to move backwards until, at last, it was pointing towards the chameleon's tail. The other one continued to point to the front.

"Most peculiar," muttered Rumble.

"Keep watching," the chameleon commanded. "I haven't finished yet."

Then the other eye began to move, not just backwards, but round and round, slowly, like a clock. And then, as Rumble's own eyes began to goggle at the weird and wonderful thing that was happening, the first eye started again. It, too, was going clockwise, but moving in the opposite direction from the first. At last, as a kind of grand finale to the act, the chameleon turned both eyes counter clockwise for a few seconds. Then he stopped and stared at the mystified rhino.

"Well?" he demanded. "Are you going to admit that flying rhinos are silly?"

"No, I'm not," protested Rumble, stoutly. "I'm quite willing to admit that moving your eyes in different directions at the same time *looks* clever, but I don't doubt I could do it if mine were wiggly like yours."

"Wiggly!" shouted the chameleon. "Wiggly! Of all the ungrateful wretches! I put on the best show you've seen in years and all you can say is, my eyes are wiggly! It's disgraceful, that's what it is! Positively disgraceful!"

Rumble took a deep breath. "Why is it," he thought, "that whenever I talk to animals they get excited?"

"Now, don't lose your wool," he said, grinning at the chameleon's warty, but quite hairless skin.

"That, I suppose, is meant to be funny," retorted his companion. "If I were a sheep, I'd laugh."

"Sorry, old chap," Rumble answered. "But, seriously, though, it really is quite clever of you to do that with your eyes. It just looked so odd, and I was startled."

"Well, if that startled you, how about this?" asked the chameleon, somewhat amazed by the rhino's handsome apology. "Tell me, what colour do you think I am?"

"Why, green, of course," Rumble replied. "In fact, you match the twig you're on perfectly."

"Watch carefully, then," the chameleon said, "and see what happens."

Slowly, the lizard crawled off the twig and lay full-length on the bare grey soil between Rumble's enormous forefeet. As the rhino watched, open-mouthed in surprise, the chameleon's colour gradually faded until in a few minutes he, too, was grey, as grey as the earth.

"Good heavens!" said Rumble. "What a thing to do!"

Without bothering to answer, the chameleon picked himself up and wandered over to a patch of elephant grass, burnt a deep yellow by the tropic sun. With very great care, he climbed the thickest stem he could find and rested, halfway up. With Rumble still staring open-mouthed, the chameleon's grey colour began to brighten. Minute after minute passed, and at last the little lizard was a yellow as the sun-parched elephant grass.

"Dear me," Rumble said, at last. "It looks as if I'm *really* going to have to apologize. You're cleverer than I thought."

"It's nothing," answered the other, modestly. "All we chameleons can change colour."

"Oh, so that's what you are," said Rumble. "You're a chameleon!"

"Exactly," answered the other, "but now, if you'll excuse me, it's time for dinner. Please stand quite still and don't make any noise."

Rumble was suddenly aware that, all the while they'd been talking, the chameleon's eyes had been twisting and turning clockwise and counter-clockwise. But now, as the seconds crept silently by, the eyes were quite still, staring at a spot about twelve inches from the end of the

reptile's nose. And, as Rumble looked at the spot where the chameleon was looking, he saw what he hadn't noticed before, a large, unhappy-looking locust perched partway up a stem of elephant grass.

In a twinkling, it wasn't there any more. Instead, the chameleon was slowly moving its jaws and appeared to have grown a mustache. Or maybe it was a beard. Rumble wasn't sure, but as he looked closer he saw it was neither. It was a fringe of grasshopper wings and, in another moment or two, even they had disappeared.

In their place the chameleon was wearing a very satisfied expression.

"Why, you horrid creature, you!" Rumble exploded. "You ate him!"

"Oh, so I did." said the chameleon, quite unconcerned. "I'm very fond of locusts, especially when they're young."

"Well, that's really unpleasant of you," snapped Rumble, who was extremely angry at the chameleon's casual manner.

"Not at all, "answered the chameleon. "You eat leaves and grass, I eat insects. And that's all there is to it. I can't help being made the way I am, any more than you can help being made the way you are."

"I suppose you'd like me to say how clever you are!" he grunted.

"Not if you don't want to," said the chameleon, reasonably. "But of course, it's not something a mere rhino could do."

"Oh, isn't it!" Rumble shouted, getting his dander up. "We'll see about that! Now, don't go away! It's about time Rumble Rhino put you in your place and showed you what's what. And that's just what Rumble Rhino's going to do!"

Then, without further ado, the great rhino closed his eyes, gave his horn three highly professional twirls, and wished. Instantly, he felt an enormous snake coiled up inside his mouth. But, no! It wasn't a snake! It was his tongue. It shot out in a twinkling, picked up a gigantic thorn bush, and stuffed it down his gullet before he could clamp his jaws shut.

"Owooeech!" he shouted, as full of prickles as a porcupine. "That wretched horn of mine! I wish I were fifty million miles away from the thing!"

And before he could say another word, he was!

Will Stratford

Dinosaurs...
They Had Their Day

Can you imagine a four-legged animal as long as eight big elephants lined up trunk-to-tail? Or a fierce flesh-eater three times as tall as a man and with teeth six inches long? Or a creature on all fours tall enough to see over one of our three-story buildings? There once were such animals. They were dinosaurs.

There are no dinosaurs now. There haven't been any for 70 million years or so. The last one died long, long before there were any people on the earth.

The word *dinosaur* comes from two Greek words that mean "terrible" and "lizard." The dinosaurs were reptiles just as lizards are, but they were not lizards. Probably the big flesh-eating dinosaurs were the fiercest animals that ever walked about. They were truly terrible. But many of the dinosaurs ate nothing but plants and were not terrible at all.

Since dinosaurs lived long before there were people, we would not know anything about them if we had not found traces of them in rocks. Traces of living things of long ago are called fossils.

Some dinosaur fossils are footprints. The footprints have come down to us through the ages in this way: As dinosaurs walked along the muddy banks of ponds and streams, they left their footprints in the mud. The mud dried and kept the footprints from being spoiled. Later more mud settled over the footprints. Thousands of years later the mud containing the prints and the layers of mud above them turned to layers of solid rock. Now when the layers are split apart the footprints can be seen.

Most of what we know about dinosaurs comes from the study of fossil bones. The dinosaur bones we find are petrified. "Petrified" means changed to stone. Some of the dinosaurs that died fell into ponds and were soon covered with mud and sand. All the soft parts of their bodies decayed. Only their bones were left. Little by little the water in the mud and sand filled up every tiny space in the bones with minerals. At last the bones were just as if they had been carved out of stone.

While the bones were changing to stone, the mud and sand around them were changing to solid rock. Most of the dinosaur bones we find have to be chiseled out of rock.

In many cases all the bones of a dinosaur have been found and have been wired together to make a skeleton. The skeleton of a dinosaur tells us a great deal about what the animal was like when it was alive. Many museums have dinosaur skeletons. Of course, a dinosaur skeleton is very heavy, since the bones are petrified.

Tyrannosaurus rex was the largest of the flesh-eating dinosaurs, but there were other flesh-eaters almost as big.

The two dinosaurs in the picture were plant-eaters. The one in the pond is *Brontosaurus*. It spent most of its time in ponds, where the water helped to hold up its heavy body. *Brontosaurus* weighed 30 tons. It was about 70 feet long.

This giant dinosaur ate water plants. It must have had to keep eating all day long to get enough food for its huge body.

The other dinosaur is *Diplodocus.* "Diplodocus" means "double beam." The crossbar of a balance for weighing things is sometimes called a beam. This dinosaur's very long neck balanced its very long tail. No one knows what colour *Diplodocus* or any other dinosaur really was.

Diplodocus is the dinosaur as long as eight elephants. So far as we know, it was the longest land animal that ever lived. From its nose to the tip of its tail it measured almost 90 feet. But *Diplodocus* was not as heavy as *Brontosaurus.*

The dinosaur tall enough to peek over a third-story roof with all four feet on the ground was another giant plant-eater—one named *Brachiosaurus.* It had a very long neck and front legs much longer than the hind ones. *Brachio* means "arm."

Brachiosaurus was the biggest four-legged animal of all time. It must have weighed 50 tons! But it wasn't the biggest animal that ever lived. Today's big blue whale is larger. The biggest blue whales are 20 feet longer than *Diplodocus* and twice as heavy as *Brachiosaurus.*

All the flesh-eating dinosaurs walked on their hind legs. You might think from the plant-eating dinosaurs you have met that all the plant-eaters went about on all fours. They didn't. *Plateosaurus,* one of the early ancestors of the giant plant-eaters, walked on its hind legs most of the time. So did *Trachodon,* the tall plant-eater. So, too, did all of *Trachodon's* close relatives.

In the Age of Reptiles there were other reptiles besides dinosaurs. *Pteranodon* was a pterosaur, or flying reptile, not a dinosaur. There were many flying reptiles.

There were reptiles that swam in the sea, too. Among them were huge turtles. There were also many marine reptiles unlike any reptiles we have today.

Dinosaur fossils have been found in almost every part of the world. Some dinosaurs seem to have lived in only a small region. Some were spread over more than one continent. *Trachodan* and its tribe, for instance, were widespread.

When dinosaurs were so common in so many places for so many millions of years, it is hard to understand why they all disappeared. Probably there is no one explanation of why they did. Here are some of the possible explanations.

In the long history of the earth there have been many changes of climate. Dinosaurs, like all reptiles, were cold-blooded. Perhaps many regions became too cold for them. But this does not explain why they died out everywhere.

The huge plant-eating dinosaurs like *Brontosaurus* spent most of their time in shallow ponds eating the plants that grew there. If the ponds dried up, these giants could not have got enough to eat and would have died off. Then the giant flesh-eaters would not have been able to get enough food and they would have disappeared. But why did all the small dinosaurs die, too?

Young dinosaurs were hatched from eggs. Some dinosaurs ate the eggs of other dinosaurs. The dinosaurs, then, may have played an important part in bringing about their own end.

Mammals, too, many have helped bring about the end of the dinosaurs. Mammals first appeared on the earth during the Age of Reptiles. The early mammals were small creatures, about the size of rats and mice. Probably many of these early mammals robbed dinosaur nests.

The plants of the earth were changing, too. Plants with woody stems were becoming common. Perhaps *Trachodon* and the other duckbills found that their many tiny teeth could not chew up the newer plants.

Even all these explanations do not make it easy to see why all the dinosaurs disappeared, when other reptiles—crocodiles, turtles, lizards and snakes, and tuatara, lone survivor of a group older than the dinosaurs—have lived on to this day.

Bertha Morris Parker

The Steadfast Tin Soldier

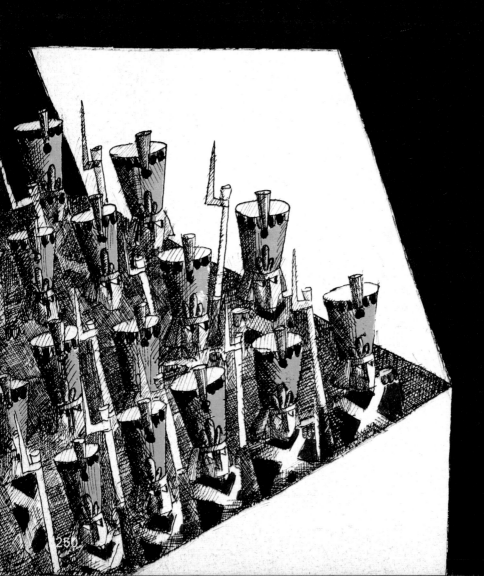

Once there were twenty-five tin soldiers. They were all brothers because they had been made from one tin spoon. They all held their rifles on their shoulders and and stood stiffly at attention. They all had red and blue uniforms and they all looked very smart.

The first thing they heard in the world was a little boy who shouted "Tin Soldiers!" when he lifted the lid of their box. The soldiers were his birthday present, and he set them up on the table right away.

Each soldier was exactly like the rest: all except one. This soldier had only one leg. He had been the last soldier made, and there hadn't been quite enough tin to finish him. But he stood just as firmly on his one leg as the others did on two.

was a cardboard castle. Through its windows you could see right into the rooms. In front of the castle there were some small trees. These were set around a mirror, which was supposed to be a lake. Some wax swans swam on the lake. It was all very pretty, but the most beautiful of all was a little lady who stood at the door of the castle.

She was dressed in a white silk gown. Over her shoulders she wore a thin blue ribbon that looked like a shawl. In the middle of the ribbon she wore a shining tinsel rose that was as big as her face. She held her arms outstretched, for she was a dancer. She kicked one leg so high in the air that it disappeared under her gown. The Tin Soldier couldn't see this leg at all. He thought she had only one leg also.

"But she is very grand and lives in a castle. I share this box with twenty-four other soldiers. It's no place for her! But I must try to meet her anyway."

Then he stretched himself out beside a snuffbox that sat on the table. From there he could watch the little dancer who still stood on one leg and never lost her balance.

That evening the other toy soldiers were put into their box. The people in the house went to bed. Then the toys began to play. The tin soldiers rattled about in their box. They wanted to join in the fun, but they couldn't lift the lid. The nutcracker turned somersaults and the crayons

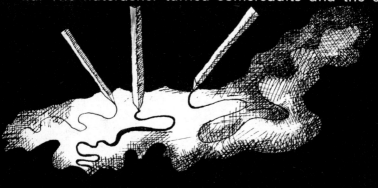

scribbled on sheets of paper. The toys made so much noise that they woke the canary, who joined in the conversation—in verse, believe it or not!

Only the Tin Soldier and the dancer stayed still. She still stood on her one leg with her arms outstretched. He stood steadfastly on his one leg, watching her.

As the clock struck twelve—POP!—a Goblin sprang out of the snuffbox. It was a trick snuffbox you see, and was meant to scare people.

"Tin Soldier!" said the Goblin. "You'd better stop your staring!"

The Tin Soldier pretended not to hear.

"All right, then, you just wait until tomorrow!" said the Goblin. And down he popped, back into the snuffbox.

The next morning the children put the Tin Soldier on the window ledge. Whether it was the Goblin or the wind that did it, nobody knows. But suddenly the window burst open and the Tin Soldier fell head over heels from the third floor. What a terrible fall! He finally landed with his leg straight up and his head jammed between two cobblestones.

The little boy rushed down immediately to look for him, but although he almost trampled him, he didn't see him. If the Soldier had shouted, he certainly would have been found. But because he was in uniform he didn't think that he should.

Soon it began to rain. The drops fell faster and faster until it was a regular downpour. When it stopped, two little boys happened to pass by.

"Look," shouted one, "a tin soldier! Let's send him on a trip." So they made a newspaper boat and sent the Tin Soldier sailing down the gutter. The rain had made huge waves in the gutter, and the current was very swift. The boat pitched and rolled so that it very nearly tipped. The Tin Soldier was quite frightened. But he didn't show it. He just held on tightly to his rifle and stood very stiffly, looking straight ahead.

Suddenly the boat plunged into a drainpipe and everything was black. "Now where am I?" thought the Soldier. "It's all that Goblin's fault. If only the little lady were here with me I wouldn't mind if it were twice as dark!"

Just then there appeared a huge water rat who lived in the pipe. "Where's your passport?" he said. "Let me see it!"

The Tin Soldier clutched his rifle tighter and didn't say a word. On rushed the boat. The rat followed it, gnashing his teeth and shouting to the twigs and sticks floating by: "Hey! Stop that soldier! He didn't pay his toll and he didn't show his passport."

The current kept getting swifter. Now the Tin Soldier could see daylight ahead. He heard a roar that would have frightened even a general. Imagine! Where the pipe ended the water went into a large canal. For the Soldier it was like being carried over a huge waterfall.

There was no escape; the boat shot out into the canal. The Tin Soldier held himself as straight as he possibly could. He didn't even blink an eyelash. The boat spun around and was soon filled to the brim with water. The Tin Soldier was up to his neck in water and the boat began to sink. Soon the paper came apart and he disappeared beneath the waves. As he sank, he thought of the dancer, whom he would never see again.

Just then a big fish came along, and swallowed him whole! It was even darker inside the fish than it had been in the pipe. And it was so cramped! But the Soldier didn't move, and still holding his rifle to his shoulder, he lay out flat on his back.

The fish tossed and thrashed, and then was very still. At last there was a flash like lightning, and the daylight appeared. A voice exclaimed, "Goodness, a tin soldier!" The fish had been caught, you see, then taken to market, and sold. Now it was in a kitchen where it had been cut open with a big knife.

The cook picked up the Tin Soldier gingerly and carried him into the living room. Everybody wanted to see the soldier who had travelled inside a fish.

They put him on the table and—believe it or not—he found himself in the very same room that he had been in before! He saw the same children, the same toys, and the same castle with the same dancer. She was still standing on one leg with the other held high in the air. She was steadfast too! The Tin Soldier was so touched that he almost cried tin tears, but that was something a soldier couldn't do. He just stood straight and looked at her. Neither of them said a word.

Suddenly, for no reason at all, one of the little boys picked up the Tin Soldier and hurled him into the fireplace. It must have been the Goblin's fault.

The Tin Soldier glowed in the flames. He felt a terrible heat, but whether it was because of the fire or because of his love he didn't know. The colours were gone from his uniform. Whether that was from his adventures or from grief nobody could say. He looked at the little lady and she looked at him. He felt himself melting away, but he still stood firm and held his rifle on his shoulder.

All at once the door opened, and a gust of wind caught the dancer. Like a nymph, she fluttered into the fire and landed right next to the Tin Soldier. In an instant, she burst into flame and was gone.

When the ashes were emptied the next day, they found the Tin Soldier. He had melted into a little tin lump the shape of a heart. But of the dancer all that remained was the tinsel rose, and that was burned black as coal.

Hans Christian Andersen

The Lama

The one-l lama,
He's a priest.
The two-l llama,
He's a beast.
And I will bet
A silk pyjama
There isn't any
Three-l lllama.

Ogden Nash

B Is For Button, Ring, and Jar

Did you ever wonder where our alphabet came from? A question such as this which may seem quite simple is really very difficult to answer. To find this answer, many scientists began studying the ruins of ancient cities. In these ruins, they found rocks and papyrus scrolls containing early forms of writing. From the study of these early written records they found that our alphabet was certainly not discovered by one person. They learned instead that it was developed over a period of thousands of years by many groups of people speaking many different languages. Like a huge jigsaw puzzle, scientists were able to fit some pieces together. But they have had to make guesses to fill in the missing parts. Even now, we still do not have a definite answer as to exactly who discovered the alphabet.

The first written messages were found around the Mediterranean Sea. If you look at a map, you can find which part of the world this is. The countries are known as Iran and Iraq today, but once were the homes of the Persians and Phoenecians. These messages were carved on rocks or pressed into moist clay tablets and left to harden. Among the buried ruins, many of these materials were found still clear enough to tell their ancient stories.

First, man used pictures to write his messages. Then later, he used marks that stood for sounds. How is it, then, that we came to use an alphabet to write our language?

Over 5000 years ago, people lived together in small groups or tribes. Except to hunt animals for food, they did not travel far from their cave homes. They often left picture messages painted on the walls of caves or scratched into stones only to tell of their hunts. But as the number of people living on earth grew, new places to live and work were found. People were no longer only hunters. They also became farmers. As they grew more food than they could use, they became traders as well.

These very first traders were the Phoenecians. Often they would sail across the Mediterranean Sea to sell food to the people living in the country of Greece. Business was good, but the Phoenecians found that they were badly in need of some way to keep records of each item they sold.

We can suppose that pictures could have been used. But can you imagine all the pictures that would have had to be drawn to show the different kinds of foods that were sold? Or all the pictures that would be needed to record the types and sizes of animals that were sold? As long as pictures were being used, people could not tell whether a cow was a young one or an old one, a big one or a small one. Some cows would be more valuable than others too. But alas, the picture writing could just show COW!

So, slowly, picture writing was replaced. And, more slowly yet, our alphabet developed. Markings that once stood for ideas became markings that stood for sounds in a word. If we can imagine that sounds in a word are like bricks in a wall, we can see how this new writing worked. To write the word David in one of the early forms of writing, we would use two bricks.

This was the type of writing that first developed in Iran. It is called cuneiform writing and was originally written with wedge-shaped tools on clay tablets.

In Egypt, a similar writing system, called heiroglyphics, was used. It contained over 500 markings. Some of these stood for ideas, as in picture writing, and others stood for sounds in words, such as DA in DA-vid.

The Phoenician sailors borrowed many marks from the Egyptian heiroglyphics to record their trade with the Greeks and Romans. The Greeks, however, made some changes to these markings and added new signs. Sounds for vowels were introduced, and now writing became much like our writing of today. For example, to write the word DAVID, the Greeks used five marks or bricks to stand for the sounds in that word.

All the different marks or symbols that stood for sounds in a spoken language came to be known as the alphabet.

The Greeks also changed the shapes of some of the marks. This was because sometimes they would write from right to left, and at other times from left to right. Slowly, the marks were turned around to resemble some of the letters we use today.

A, α —Alpha   O, o —Omikron

E, ε —Epsilon   Y, υ —Upsilon

H, η —Eta   Ω, ω —Omega

I, ι —Iota

The Greeks added symbols to the alphabet which stood for vowel sounds.

V	5
X	10
L	50
C	100
D	500
M	1000

The alphabet underwent further changes by the Roman people. (Long ago, the people who lived near the city of Rome in Italy were called Romans.) The Romans used brushes to write with paper scrolls to write on. As a result, they rounded off some of the shapes of the Greek letters. Many of the letters of our English alphabet have come from the old Roman alphabet. The Romans used some of the letters of their alphabet to stand for numbers as well. That is why Roman numerals look like letters of the alphabet.

The Romans used the alphabet signs to stand for both sounds and numbers.

As the Greeks and Romans travelled into Europe, their alphabet was borrowed by people who spoke many different languages. These European people changed the shape of some of the letters and added in letters to stand for sounds in their native tongue. Here are some letters of the alphabet which stand for the same sound in the Greek, English and Russian languages. Are there any exactly the same?

Greek	English	Russian
Δ, δ	D d	Д д
Γ, γ	G g	Γ г
Κ, κ	K k	К к
Λ, λ	L l	Л л
Μ, μ	M m	М м
Ν, ν	N n	Н н
Π, π	P p	П п
Ρ, ρ	R r	Р р
Τ, τ	T t	Т т

If you are just learning how to read and write English, you learn that the symbol or letter   b   stands for the first sound in the word button. French children learn that   b   stands for the sound heard at the beginning of *bague* (bahg), which means *ring*. Russian children learn that this sound is written with the letter   б   as in банка(bahnkah) which means jar. So you see,   b   really can be for button, bague (ring) and банка (jar).

Would you like to hear yourself speak in other languages? Just say the sounds written in the brackets below these sentences:

Good morning!
GREEK: Καλημέρα.
          (Kah-lee-MEN-rah)
FRENCH: Bonjour!
          (Bohn-zhoor)
RUSSIAN: доброе утро
          (Doh-broh-yeh OO-trah)
GERMAN: Guten Morgen!
          (Goo-t'n MOHR-g'n)

I am happy to meet you.
GREEK: Χαίρω πολύ.
          (HEH-roh pol-LEE)
FRENCH: Énchanté de faire votre connaissance.
          (Awn-shan-teh duh fehr vohtr
          kon-neh-sawns)
RUSSIAN: Очень рада
          (OH-chen RAH-dah)
GERMAN: Sehr erfreut.
          (Zehr ehr-FROYT)

What is your name?
GREEK: Τ' ὄνομά σας;
          (Toh-nah-MAH sahs)
FRENCH: Quel est votre nom?
          (Kel eh vohtre nohng?)
RUSSIAN: Как ваше имя?
          (Kahk vAH-sheh EE-m'yah)
GERMAN: Wie ist Ihr Name?
          (Vee ist eer NAH-meh)

How are you?
GREEK: Πῶς εἶσθε;
(Pohs EES-th'eh)
FRENCH: Comment allez-vous?
(Koh-mawng tah-leh-voo)
RUSSIAN: Как поживаете?
(Kahk pah-zhee-VAH-yeh-t'yeh)
GERMAN: Wie geht es Ihnen?
(Vee gait ess EE-n'n)

Good-bye!
GREEK: 'Αντίο
(Ah-DEE-oh)
FRENCH: Au revoir!
(Oh ruh-vwar)
RUSSIAN: До свиданья
(Dah-svee-DAH-n'yah)
GERMAN: Auf wiedersehen!
(Owf VEE-der-zay'n)

Janet Trischuk

The Boyhood of a Storyteller

"My tea is nearly ready, and the sun has left the sky;
It's time to take the window and see Leerie going by;
For every night at tea-time and before you take your seat
With lantern and with ladder he comes posting up the
street."

"What luck it is to have a lamp before our very own door,"
thought little Louis Stevenson. He was standing by the
nursery window, watching for the lamplighter.

One by one the lamps along Howard Place, Edinburgh,
were touched into points of light. Finally the lamplighter
reached No. 8. For Louis, this was the crowning joy of all.
Would the lamplighter look up and see the small face
pressed against the window, and nod good evening?
Or would he be too busy?

It was no wonder that the coming of the lamplighter
was so eagerly looked for! The winter days were often
long and wearisome to the little boy shut up in the
nursery there. But everything he could see from his
window was interesting and exciting.

Louis was often ill. He caught cold so easily in the
bitter cold Edinburgh winds, that he was often kept
indoors the whole winter through. All that he saw of the
outside world was through his nursery window.

Many other days Louis had to stay in bed. He was
obliged to make-believe a good deal to keep himself
happy, as he sat up with a sweater pinned around his
shoulders and his toys arranged on the counterpane
beside him.

But there was always someone at hand ready to comfort him. His nurse, "Cummie" as he called her, never failed him. She was always there to soothe the pain, always patient and always gentle with the poor weary boy. His nurseries changed from one house to another, but Cummie was always there. He never forgot the feeling of "her most comfortable hand."

With Mother and Cummie to amuse him all day long, he was rather like a small prince in the nursery. And his will and pleasure was to have someone read to him constantly.

He never could listen quietly to any story. He always wanted to act it—slaying dragons, attacking the enemy, galloping off on a fiery horse to carry news to the enemy— until he was tired out. Then Cummie would smooth back the hair from his hot forehead, and try to persuade him to rest.

But it was not only Cummie who watched over and cared for little Louis. There were his father and his mother too. Often during the night the nursery door would open gently. His father would come in and tell him story after story, until the child forgot his pain and weariness and drifted off to sleep.

274   *(Stevenson with his family and household in Samoa)*

Then there was his young mother, who was so ready to play with him. She made even the dull nursery a sunshiny, happy place. She was not very strong, and Louis began early to try to take care of her.

When spring came, Louis played about his grandfather's garden in the country near Edinburgh. Like the flowers, he began to lift up his head and grow strong in the sunshine.

It was a different world to Louis when the sun shone and the sky was blue. The splendid colours of the flowers made his days a rainbow riot of delight. There was no more lying in bed and no more coughs. Instead, he spent long warm summer days in the garden, or down by the river.

There were cousins there too, ready to play all the games that Louis invented, to lie behind the bushes with toy guns watching for a drove of antelopes to go by, or to be shipwrecked sailors on a desert island.

There, too, was a kind aunt who brought out crackers and jelly at eleven o'clock from her storeroom, which always had so delicious a smell of raisins and spices. Never did anything taste so good as those crackers and that jelly.

One fall when Louis went home, he took a companion with him. His cousin, Robert Alan Stevenson, spent a whole winter with him, and together they lived in a make-believe world of their own. Robert Alan made even the grey days seem cheerful.

Disagreeable things were turned into delightful play, and even their meals were interesting. Instead of having to eat up a plateful of uninteresting porridge for breakfast, the magic of make-believe turned it into a foreign land, covered with snow (which was the sugar of course), or an island that was threatened by the encroaching sea (that was the cream).

The excitement of seeing the dry land disappearing or the snow mountains being cleared was so entrancing that the porridge was eaten up before the magic came to an end. Even cold mutton could be charmed into something quite delicious when Louis called it red venison, and described the mighty hunter who had gone forth and shot down the deer after many desperate adventures.

But perhaps the greatest joy of all was when Saturday afternoons came round. On Saturdays the boys went down to Leith to look at the ships, always the chief delight of their hearts. Passing down Leith Walk, they first came to a stationer's shop at the corner. In the window there stood a tiny toy theatre, and piled about it a heap of playbooks.

Happy indeed was the child who had a penny to spend, who could walk into the shop with assurance and ask to see those books. Many a time Louis stood longingly outside, trying to see the outside pictures and to read as much of the printing as could be seen.

Those little books opened to Louis the golden world of romance, the doors of which were never closed to him again.

It was not until Louis was eight years old that he began to read. His mother and Cummie had always been ready to read to him, and that, he thought, was the pleasanter way. But quite suddenly he discovered that it was good to be able to read stories to himself. It was a red-letter day when he first got possession of the "Arabian Nights."

Long before he could write, he was fond of dictating stories to anyone who would write them for him. Poor patient Cummie would write sheet after sheet of nonsense, all of which she treasured and read to his mother afterward.

The school days of Louis Stevenson made but little impression upon him. He was so often kept away by ill health, and the schools were so often changed, that he did not win many laurels there. Whatever he liked to learn he learned with all his heart, and to the rest he gave very little attention. His love of make-believe was richly evident in his early literary efforts at Edinburgh University. By the time he had finished his studies, he was a well-known author.

He will always be popular with children who have read his "Child's Garden of Verses," "Treasure Island," and "Kidnapped."

Critics pronounced him "the greatest writer of romance of his day," with a charming sense of beauty and humour. The flights of his imagination began with the magic make-believe of his childhood.

Amy Steedman

The Land of Counterpane

When I was sick and lay a-bed,
I had two pillows at my head,
And all my toys beside me lay
To keep me happy all the day.

And sometimes for an hour or so
I watched my leaden soldiers go,
With different uniforms and drills,
Among the bed-clothes, through the hills.

And sometimes sent my ships in fleets
All up and down among the sheets;
Or brought my trees and houses out,
And planted cities all about.

I was the giant great and still
That sits upon the pillow-hill,
And sees before him, dale and plain,
The pleasant land of counterpane.

Robert Louis Stevenson